LATIN'S NOT SO TOUGH!

LEVEL SIX

A Classical Latin Worktext
by
Karen Mohs

Dear Parent/Teacher:

Welcome to the Latin Workbook Level Six!

In this workbook, students review the Latin alphabet, vocabulary, and grammar taught in Levels One through Five. Infinitives, personal pronouns, cardinal and ordinal numerals, special case uses, passive voice, and imperfect and future tenses are introduced, along with additional vocabulary. The sentences are contrived and simplified to afford practice with the forms the student has learned.

Remove the flashcard pages at the end of the workbook, cut out the words, and paste or tape them onto 3 by 5 inch cards. Review flashcards from the Level Five flashcard deck, beginning on page 3. Flashcards are introduced for Level Six on page 15. Your student should check the box at the bottom of each page when daily flashcard work is completed. Please refer to "Flashcard Tips" in the appendix.

Please take a moment to look through the appendix pages. There you will find a glossary, an index, and other helpful resources. An answer key is available, as well as quizzes/exams and flashcards on a ring.

Keep having fun!

References:
First Year Latin by Charles Jenney, Jr.
Second Year Latin by Charles Jenney, Jr.
The New College Latin & English Dictionary by John C. Traupman, Ph.D.
Latin Grammar by B.L. Gildersleeve & G. Lodge
New Latin Grammar by Charles E. Bennett
501 Latin Verbs by Richard E. Prior and Joseph Wohlberg

ISBN-13: 978-1-931842-88-4
ISBN-10: 1-931842-88-4

Greek 'n' Stuff
P.O. Box 882
Moline, IL 61266-0882
www.greeknstuff.com

This Level Six Latin Workbook
belongs to:

_____

(student's name)

TABLE OF CONTENTS

Appendix

LATIN PRONUNCIATION REVIEW

Match the Latin letters to their sounds.

su	**s** in *sit*	V v	**w** in *way*
T t	**su** in *suave*	Z z	form lips to say "**oo**," say "**ee**" instead (held longer)
th	**th** in *thick*	Ȳ ȳ	**ph** in *phone*
S s	**u** in *rule*	Y y	**dz** in *adze*
N n	**m** in *man*	ph	**c** in *cat*
M m	**t** in *tag*	C c	form lips to say "**oo**," say "**ee**" instead (held shorter)
H h	**n** in *nut*	ch	*pt*
Ū ū	**u** in *put*	P p	*ps*
au	**h** in *hat*	bt	**i** in *sit*
U u	**oy** in *joy*	I i	**i** in *machine*
oe	**ow** in *now*	bs	**ch** in *character*
Q q	**qu** in *quit*	B b	**p** in *pit*
gu	**a** in *father*	Ī ī	**b** in *boy*
F f	**r** in *run*	Ē ē	**ey** in *obey*
A a	**gu** in *anguish*	eu	**e** in *bet*
Ā ā	**f** in *fan*	E e	**d** in *dog*
R r	**a** in *idea*	D d	*ay-oo* as one syllable
K k	**ks** in *socks*	O o	**o** in *note**
L l	**k** in *king*	Ō ō	**o** in *omit**
i	**y** in *youth*	ae	**uee** in *queen*
X x	**g** in *go*	ei	**ei** in *neighbor*
G g	**l** in *land*	ui	*aye*

*Although both Latin "o" sounds are **long**, the ō as in *note* is held longer than the o as in *omit*.

LATIN PRONUNCIATION REVIEW

Write the Latin letters for the sounds.

1. _____ *pt*

2. _____ **oy** in *joy*

3. _____ **ey** in *obey*

4. _____ **u** in *rule*

5. _____ **ei** in *neighbor*

6. _____ **i** in *machine*

7. _____ form lips to say "**oo**," say "**ee**" instead (held shorter)

8. _____ **ph** in *phone*

9. _____ **p** in *pit*

10. _____ **a** in *father*

11. _____ **s** in *sit*

12. _____ **w** in *way*

13. _____ **c** in *cat*

14. _____ **y** in *youth*

15. _____ **o** in *omit*

16. _____ **h** in *hat*

17. _____ **e** in *bet*

18. _____ **ch** in *character*

19. _____ **gu** in *anguish*

20. _____ **i** in *sit*

21. _____ *aye*

22. _____ *ay-oo* as one syllable

23. _____ **k** in *king*

24. _____ **ks** in *socks*

25. _____ **a** in *idea*

26. _____ **o** in *note*

27. _____ **th** in *thick*

28. _____ **uee** in *queen*

29. _____ **dz** in *adze*

30. _____ form lips to say "**oo**," say "**ee**" instead (held longer)

31. _____ **su** in *suave*

32. _____ **f** in *fan*

33. _____ **g** in *go*

34. _____ **ow** in *now*

35. _____ *ps*

36. _____ **u** in *put*

VOCABULARY REVIEW

Match the Latin words to their meanings.

lūdus	island		servus	slave
īnsula	letter		cōpia	field
littera	law		campus	cause
lēgātus	game		silva	plenty
lēx	place		socius	troops
lingua	lieutenant		causa	comrade
locus	tongue		cōpiae	forest
amīcitia	farmer		poena	boy
agricola	friendliness		porta	country
audācia	water		patria	poet
aqua	daring		puella	province
amīcus	year		poēta	gate
annus	field		puer	penalty
ager	friend		prōvincia	girl
fuga	fortune		vīlla	life
fīlius	flight		verbum	road
fīlia	son		urbs	word
fortūna	daughter		vīta	city
fāma	report		vēritās	farmhouse
fābula	story		vir	truth
fēmina	woman		via	man
dō	I defend		āmittō	I love
dīcō	I give		agō	I stroll
dēmōnstrō	I tell		appellō	I address
dēlectō	I show		amō	I do
dēligō	I please		ambulō	I receive
dūcō	I choose		audiō	I lose
dēfendō	I lead		accipiō	I hear

☐ Flashcards (Review these vocabulary words from the Level Four and Level Five flashcard decks. Check the box each day when you practice your flashcards.)

VOCABULARY REVIEW

Write the Latin words.

story	_____	friendship	_____
supply	_____	ambassador	_____
ally	_____	I grant	_____
exile	_____	I drive	_____
I name	_____	punishment	_____
year	_____	play	_____
location	_____	forces	_____
I accept	_____	language	_____
plain	_____	chance	_____
I like	_____	boldness	_____
husband	_____	reason	_____
I say	_____	villa	_____
I choose	_____	I walk	_____
I bring	_____	rumor	_____
wife	_____	native land	_____
trueness	_____	I point out	_____
I listen to	_____	territory	_____
I defend	_____	street	_____

☐ Flashcards

Latin Workbook - Level 6
Copyright © 2006 by Karen Mohs

VOCABULARY REVIEW

Match the Latin words to their meanings.

superō	I defeat	capiō*	I call together
exspectō	I await	cōnstituō	I shout
stō	I save	convocō	I capture
spectō	I stand	clāmō	I set up
sedeō	I look at	cupiō	I move
scrībō	I sit	cōnfirmō	I strengthen
servō	I write	cēdō	I wish
portō	I put	nāvigō	I stay
pōnō	I finish	moveō	I tell
perficiō	I carry	nārrō	I send
pugnō	I fight	moneō	I sail
habitō	I prepare	maneō	I move
parō	I consider	mittō	I report
habeō	I live	nūntiō	I inform
videō	I am victorious	laudō	I set free
vulnerō	I call	iūdicō	I labor
edō	I fly	inveniō	I consider
volō	I eat	labōrō	I praise
vocō	I wound	iaciō	I find
vincō	I see	līberō	I kill
veniō	I come	interficiō	I throw
numerus	number	cōnsilium*	horn
memoria	king	caelum	captive
rēx	sailor	cūra	plan
nauta	queen	cornū	sky
nūntius	nature	carrus	care
rēgina	messenger	captīvus	wagon
nātūra	memory	clārus	bright

*The words cōnsilium and capiō together mean *make a plan* or *form a plan*.

☐ Flashcards - (Add these vocabulary cards from the Level Five flashcard deck.)

VOCABULARY REVIEW

Write the Latin words.

I eat	I remain
I surpass	I judge
I let go	I come upon
I take	I set
I have	I suffer
I encourage	I yield
I relate	cart
I free	I wait for
I accomplish	I want
I announce	message
I warn	famous
wing (army)	I prepare for
group	heavens
I throw	I guard
I dwell	I affect
prisoner	I summon
I determine	I conquer
anxiety	foresight

☐ Flashcards

VOCABULARY REVIEW

Match the Latin words to their meanings.

ecce	yesterday	atque	nevertheless
herī	behold	tamen	now
quid	tomorrow	iam	for
hōra	what?	nam	then
crās	hour	quod	well
nunc	badly	tum	because
male	now	bene	and also
ad	down from	dux	leader
ob	to	dīligentia	diligence
et	because of	dōnum	god
ab	by	tuba	trumpet
dē	and	deus	gift
est	he is	dominus	master
in	into	diēs	day
sed	but	mors	name
ubi	for a long time	manus	hand
diū	where?	māter	mother
cum	along with	nōmen	death
ergō	why?	magister	teacher
cūr	therefore	mare	night
nōn	not	nox	sea
semper	often	exitus	horse
saepe	after that time	gaudium	joy
hodiē	today	gladius	sword
posteā	always	equus	departure
etiam	meanwhile	epistula	earth
quōmodo	also	gēns	nation
interim	how?	terra	letter

☐ Flashcards - (Add these vocabulary cards from the Level Five flashcard deck.)

VOCABULARY REVIEW

Write the Latin words.

owner	_____	today	_____
guide	_____	gladness	_____
director	_____	already	_____
yet	_____	always	_____
night	_____	behold	_____
fully	_____	insufficiently	_____
yesterday	_____	at that time	_____
near	_____	often	_____
meanwhile	_____	concerning	_____
family	_____	death	_____
out of	_____	outcome	_____
mother	_____	away from	_____
present	_____	hour	_____
band (of men)	_____	and even	_____
on account of	_____	tomorrow	_____
land	_____	onto	_____
afterward	_____	sea	_____
sword	_____	with	_____

☐ Flashcards

VOCABULARY REVIEW

Match the Latin words to their meanings.

pater	battle	iānua	route
proelium	nations	inter	door
potestās	father	iter*	want
populī	people	iūdex	between
pecūnia	power	inopia	anger
populus	harbor	ibi	there
portus	wealth	īra	juror
lectus	book	animus	mind
homō	dining couch	arbor	animal
liber	human being	animal	bird
hostis	stone	arma	tree
hortus	enemy	animī	arrival
lapis	the enemy (pl.)	avis	weapons
hostēs	garden	adventus	courage
soror	sister	meus	good
sella	hope	miser	middle of
clāmor	chair	altus	many
cēna	shout	multī	your
spēs	senate	tuus	high
cibus	dinner	bonus	my
senātus	food	medius	unhappy
sciō	I do	vester	quick
dormiō	they are	celer	your
faciō*	I inform	noster	sharp
surgō	I rise	ācer	our
currō	I know	sinister	beautiful
sunt	I sleep	pulcher	right
doceō	I run	dexter	left

*The words iter and faciō together mean **march**.

☐ Flashcards - (Add these vocabulary cards from the Level Five flashcard deck.)

VOCABULARY REVIEW

Write the Latin words.

port	wrath
stone	tree
money	swift
noble	there are
arms	dinner
good	approach
I stand up	opportunity
ours	spirit
journey	wretched
I run	seat
tribes	left-hand
in that place	bed
poverty	human being
deep	I make
noise	mine
right-hand	tribe
among	garden
I sleep	fierce

☐ Flashcards

VOCABULARY REVIEW

Match the Latin words to their meanings.

regō	I rule	sacra	immediately
relinquō	I leave	sub	like
respondeō	I seize	similis	rituals
rapiō	I answer	statim	under
reperiō	I hold back	sacer	holy
retineō	I give back	sine	over
reddō	I find	super	without
flōs	grain	perīculum	wisely
frūmentum	window	patrēs	danger
frāter	faith	per	senators
fenestra	flower	praemium	through
fēlīciter	brother	prūdenter	behind
fidēs	wave	post	bread
fluctus	happily	pānis	reward
oppidum	speech	parvus	happy
audācter	boldly	fēlix	powerful
omnis	town	fortis	foresighted
ōrātiō	I seize	prūdēns	faithful
oppugnō	I attack	fidēlis	brave
audāx	every	facilis	small
occupō	daring	potēns	easy
mēnsa	much	teneō	I try
medicus	bad	trīstis	sad
magnus	large	trādō	I hand over
mūrus	wall	trāns	across
multitūdō	great number	temptō	I hold
malus	doctor	terreō	I frighten
multus*	table	itaque	therefore

*When multus and a second adjective modify the same noun, the conjunction et is used to join the two adjectives.

☐ Flashcards - (Add these vocabulary cards from the Level Five flashcard deck.)

VOCABULARY REVIEW

Write the Latin words.

at once _____

grim _____

loyalty _____

prudently _____

I leave behind _____

above _____

loyal _____

physician _____

loaf _____

bold _____

flower _____

evil _____

fortunate _____

I discover _____

by means of _____

similar _____

course _____

reward _____

great _____

little _____

I hold back _____

I snatch _____

I rule _____

rashly _____

wise _____

sacred _____

I reply _____

close under _____

I surrender _____

successfully _____

I attempt _____

risk _____

I restore _____

and so _____

crowd _____

after _____

☐ Flashcards

12

VOCABULARY REVIEW

Match the Latin words to their meanings.

adhūc	and ... not		ē	against	
maximē	greatly		brevis	both ... and	
ante	not yet		contrā	heavy	
neque	still		gerō	short	
magnopere	most		gravis	from	
nōndum	before		et ... et	I bear	
lātus	tired		nec	away from	
longus	epistle		ā	nor	
litterae	long		ex	out of	
validus	happy		numquam	never	
laetus	strong		aut	where	
dēfessus	wide		ubi	or	

Match the Latin phrases and clauses to their meanings.

ā dextrō cornū	until late at night
nōn sōlum ... sed etiam	not only ... but also
ā sinistrō cornū	on the right wing
ad multam noctem	on the left wing
brevī tempore	for which reason
quā dē causā	in a short time
ōrātiōnem habeō	I deliver a speech

memoriā teneō	I break camp		simul atque	late at night
diem cōnstituō	I give thanks		nāvis longa	battleship
neque ... neque	I appoint a day		ā tergō	late in the day
castra ... moveō	neither ... nor		multā nocte	in the rear
secunda mēnsa	I wage war		ā dextrā	as soon as
bellum gerō	I remember		multō diē	either ... or
grātiās agō	dessert		aut ... aut	on the right

☐ Flashcards - (Add these vocabulary cards from the Level Five flashcard deck.)

VOCABULARY REVIEW

Write the Latin words, phrases, or clauses.

opposite _____

in front of _____

in the rear _____

joyful _____

battleship _____

I carry on _____

late in the day _____

I give thanks _____

either ... or _____

brief _____

on the right _____

late at night _____

especially _____

as soon as _____

strong _____

severe _____

I wage war _____

broad _____

until late at night _____

dessert _____

I appoint a day _____

I remember _____

I break camp _____

I deliver a speech _____

not only ... but also _____

for which reason _____

in a short time _____

☐ Flashcards

GRAMMAR REVIEW
Present Active Indicative Verbs

Principal Parts

The four main parts of a Latin verb are called its ***principal parts***.

1st principal part of amō	2nd principal part of amō	3rd principal part of amō	4th principal part of amō
amō	**amāre**	**amāvī**	**amātum**
This is the part most dictionaries use to list the word.	Remove the -re to find the present stem in three of the four conjugations.	Remove the -ī to find the perfect stem, which is used in the perfect system.	This part is called the supine. It functions as a verbal noun.

First Conjugation Verbs

(Second principal part ends in -āre. Drop -re from the second principal part to find the present stem [amā-].)

	Singular		Plural	
1st Person	amō means	**I like.**	amāmus means	**We like.**
2nd Person	amās means	**You** (singular) **like.**	amātis means	**You** (plural) **like.**
3rd Person	amat means	**He (she, it) likes.**	amant means	**They like.**

Second Conjugation Verbs

(Second principal part ends in -ēre. Drop -re from the second principal part to find the present stem [sedē-].)

	Singular		Plural	
1st Person	sedeō means	**I sit.**	sedēmus means	**We sit.**
2nd Person	sedēs means	**You** (s.) **sit.**	sedētis means	**You** (pl.) **sit.**
3rd Person	sedet means	**He (she, it) sits.**	sedent means	**They sit.**

Translate these Latin words.

docet _____   docēs _____

docent _____   docēmus _____

doceō _____   docētis _____

☐ Flashcards (New Level Six flashcards are located at the back of this workbook. Add the cards for this page. Occasionally review the vocabulary in the Level Five flashcard deck.)

First Declension Nouns

(Genitive singular ends in -ae. First declension nouns are usually feminine, but sometimes masculine.)
(Drop the -ae from the genitive singular to find the stem [puell-].)

Singular

Nominative	puella	means	**the girl** (*subject of sentence*)
Genitive	puellae	means	**of the girl** (*shows possession*)
Dative	puellae	means	**to (or for) the girl** (*indirect object*)
Accusative	puellam	means	**the girl** (*direct object*)
Ablative	cum puellā	means	**with the girl** (*ablative of accompaniment*)

Plural

Nominative	puellae	means	**the girls** (*subject of sentence*)
Genitive	puellārum	means	**of the girls** (*shows possession*)
Dative	puellīs	means	**to (or for) the girls** (*indirect object*)
Accusative	puellās	means	**the girls** (*direct object*)
Ablative	cum puellīs	means	**with the girls** (*ablative of accompaniment*)

Write the correct form of sella in the blanks.

1. **The chairs** have four legs.

2. The man wants **the chairs**.

3. The legs **of the chair** are wooden.

4. The man wants **the chair**.

5. The legs **of the chairs** are wooden.

6. The seamstress makes cushions **for the chairs**.

7. **The chair** has four legs.

8. The seamstress makes a cushion **for the chair**.

☐ Flashcards - (Add the new cards.)

GRAMMAR REVIEW
Declensions

Second Declension Nouns - Masculine

(Genitive singular ends in -ī. Second declension nouns are usually masculine, but sometimes neuter.)
(Drop the -ī from the genitive singular to find the stem [amīc-].)

Nominative singular ending in -us

	Singular			Plural		
Nom.	amīcus	means	**the friend**	amīcī	means	**the friends**
Gen.	amīcī	means	**of the friend**	amīcōrum	means	**of the friends**
Dat.	amīcō	means	**to (or for) the friend**	amīcīs	means	**to (or for) the friends**
Acc.	amīcum	means	**the friend**	amīcōs	means	**the friends**
Abl.	cum amīcō	means	**with the friend**	cum amīcīs	means	**with the friends**

Nominative singular ending in -ius

(The expected genitive singular -iī of these -ius nouns is shortened to -ī. However, the stem retains the -i- [soci-].)

Nom.	socius	means	**the comrade**	sociī	means	**the comrades**
Gen.	socī	means	**of the comrade**	sociōrum	means	**of the comrades**
Dat.	sociō	means	**to (or for) the comrade**	sociīs	means	**to (or for) the comrades**
Acc.	socium	means	**the comrade**	sociōs	means	**the comrades**
Abl.	cum sociō	means	**with the comrade**	cum sociīs	means	**with the comrades**

Match the words to their meanings.

lūdōrum	with the doctors	fenestrārum	of the swords
numerum	the horse	nūntiōs	of the windows
cum medicīs	of the games	captīvus	the messengers
equus	of the carts	gladiōrum	the captive
mūrōs	the number	lectum	with the food
carrōrum	the chairs	cum cibō	the lieutenant
sellās	the walls	amīcōrum	of the comrades
cum dominīs	of the son	lēgātus	of the friends
hortum	the garden	iānua	the dining couch
filī	with the masters	sociōrum	the door

☐ Flashcards - (Add the new cards.)

GRAMMAR REVIEW
Case Uses

Ablative of Place Where
(To indicate location, use the prepositions in or sub with the ablative case.)

Singular

In īnsulā puella habitat.
The girl lives *on the island.*

Sub vīllā animal habitat.
The animal lives *under the villa.*

Plural

In lūdīs puella habitat.
The girl lives *in the schools.*

Sub vīllīs animal habitat.
The animal lives *under the villas.*

Ablative of Means or Instrument
(To indicate the means or instrument by which something is done, use the ablative case without a preposition.)
(English prepositions such as **with**, **in**, or **on** can be used, but the idea of this construction is ***by means of**.*)

Singular

Puellās tubā convocō.
I summon the girls *with
(by means of) the trumpet.*

Plural

Puellās tubīs convocō.
I summon the girls *with
(by means of) the trumpets.*

Ablative of Manner
(To indicate the manner in which an action is performed, use the preposition cum with the ablative case.)
(The English preposition **with** can be used, but the idea of this construction is the ***manner*** in which a thing is done.)

Cum audāciā pugnō.
I fight *with boldness.*

(When an adjective is used with the Ablative of Manner, the preposition cum may be used or may be omitted.)
(If cum *is* used, it is placed between the adjective and the noun.)

Correct: magnā cum audāciā
with great boldness

Correct: magnā audāciā
with great boldness

Ablative of Accompaniment
(To indicate accompaniment, use the preposition cum with the ablative case.)

Singular

Cum fēminā puella ambulat.
The girl walks *with the woman.*

Plural

Cum fēminīs puella ambulat.
The girl walks *with the women.*

☐ Flashcards - (Add the new cards.)

GRAMMAR REVIEW
Declensions

More Second Declension Nouns - Masculine
(Genitive singular ends in -ī. Second declension nouns are usually masculine, but sometimes neuter.)

Nominative singular ending in -er
(Some second declension nouns retain the vowel in the stem.)
(Drop the -ī from the genitive singular to find the stem [puer-].)

	Singular			Plural		
Nom.	puer	means	**the boy**	puerī	means	**the boys**
Gen.	puerī	means	**of the boy**	puerōrum	means	**of the boys**
Dat.	puerō	means	**to (or for) the boy**	puerīs	means	**to (or for) the boys**
Acc.	puerum	means	**the boy**	puerōs	means	**the boys**
Abl.	cum puerō	means	**with the boy**	cum puerīs	means	**with the boys**

(Some second declension nouns do not retain the vowel in the stem.)
(Drop the -ī from the genitive singular to find the stem [agr-].)

Nom.	ager	means	**the field**	agrī	means	**the fields**
Gen.	agrī	means	**of the field**	agrōrum	means	**of the fields**
Dat.	agrō	means	**to (or for) the field**	agrīs	means	**to (or for) the fields**
Acc.	agrum	means	**the field**	agrōs	means	**the fields**
Abl.	in agrō	means	**in the field**	in agrīs	means	**in the fields**

Circle the correct Latin words.

the teachers	of the books	the fields
magistrīs	librōrum	agrīs
magistrum	librīs	agrī
magistrōs	librum	agrō

of the boy	for the teacher	for the books
puerī	magistrī	librōs
puerōs	magistrō	librōrum
puerum	magister	librīs

☐ Flashcards - (Add the new cards.)

GRAMMAR REVIEW
Present Active Indicative Verbs

Third Conjugation Verbs

(Second principal part ends in -ere. Drop -ō from the first principal part to find the present stem [dīc-].)

	Singular			Plural	
1st Person	dīcō	means	**I say.**	dīcimus	means	**We say.**
2nd Person	dīcis	means	**You (s.) say.**	dīcitis	means	**You (pl.) say.**
3rd Person	dīcit	means	**He (she, it) says.**	dīcunt	means	**They say.**

Notice the -i- or the -u- inserted between the present tense stem and the ending in all but the first word. This avoids the awkward pronunciation of an ending placed directly after a consonant.

Third Conjugation I-Stem Verbs

(Second principal part ends in -ere. Drop -ō from the first principal part to find the present stem [capi-].)
(The stem of third conjugation i-stem verbs ends in -i-.)

	Singular			Plural	
1st Person	capiō	means	**I take.**	capimus	means	**We take.**
2nd Person	capis	means	**You (s.) take.**	capitis	means	**You (pl.) take.**
3rd Person	capit	means	**He (she, it) takes.**	capiunt	means	**They take.**

Circle the correct words.

1. The Latin word currō is the (first, second, third, fourth) principal part of the (first, second, third, third i-stem) conjugation verb currō.

2. The Latin word rapere is the (first, second, third, fourth) principal part of the (first, second, third, third i-stem) conjugation verb rapiō.

3. The Latin word territum is the (first, second, third, fourth) principal part of the (first, second, third, third i-stem) conjugation verb terreō.

4. The Latin word perfēcī is the (first, second, third, fourth) principal part of the (first, second, third, third i-stem) conjugation verb perficiō.

5. The Latin word iūdicāvī is the (first, second, third, fourth) principal part of the (first, second, third, third i-stem) conjugation verb iūdicō.

☐ Flashcards - (Add the new cards.)

GRAMMAR REVIEW
Declensions

Third Declension Nouns - Masculine and Feminine
(Genitive singular ends in -is.)

(Some third declension nouns retain the vowel in the stem.)
(Drop the -is from the genitive singular to find the stem [sorōr-].)

	Singular			Plural		
Nom.	soror	means	**the sister**	sorōrēs	means	**the sisters**
Gen.	sorōris	means	**of the sister**	sorōrum	means	**of the sisters**
Dat.	sorōrī	means	**to (or for) the sister**	sorōribus	means	**to (or for) the sisters**
Acc.	sorōrem	means	**the sister**	sorōrēs	means	**the sisters**
Abl.	cum sorōre	means	**with the sister**	cum sorōribus	means	**with the sisters**

(Some third declension nouns do not retain the vowel in the stem.)
(Drop the -is from the genitive singular to find the stem [frātr-].)

Nom.	frāter	means	**the brother**	frātrēs	means	**the brothers**
Gen.	frātris	means	**of the brother**	frātrum	means	**of the brothers**
Dat.	frātrī	means	**to (or for) the brother**	frātribus	means	**to (or for) the brothers**
Acc.	frātrem	means	**the brother**	frātrēs	means	**the brothers**
Abl.	cum frātre	means	**with the brother**	cum frātribus	means	**with the brothers**

Add the correct endings to the Latin nouns.

Dative Plural

lect _____

iānu _____

iūdic _____

Genitive Singular

ōratiōn _____

mūr _____

īr _____

Ablative Singular

sell _____

de _____

flōr _____

Accusative Plural

mēns _____

arbor _____

cib _____

Dative Singular

hort _____

fenestr _____

noct _____

Genitive Plural

clāmōr _____

medic _____

cēn _____

☐ Flashcards - (Add the new cards.)

GRAMMAR REVIEW
Declensions

Third Declension I-Stem Nouns - Masculine and Feminine
(Genitive singular ends in -is. Genitive plural ends in -ium.)
(Drop the -is from the genitive singular to find the stem [host- or gent- or urb-].)

Nominative singular ending in -ēs or -is
(with same number of syllables in nominative and genitive cases)

	Singular			Plural		
Nom.	hostis	means	**the enemy**	hostēs	means	**the enemies**
Gen.	hostis	means	**of the enemy**	hostium	means	**of the enemies**
Dat.	hostī	means	**to (or for) the enemy**	hostibus	means	**to (or for) the enemies**
Acc.	hostem	means	**the enemy**	hostēs	means	**the enemies**
Abl.	cum hoste	means	**with the enemy**	cum hostibus	means	**with the enemies**

Nominative singular ending in -ns or -rs

Nom.	gēns	means	**the nation**	gentēs	means	**the nations**
Gen.	gentis	means	**of the nation**	gentium	means	**of the nations**
Dat.	gentī	means	**to (or for) the nation**	gentibus	means	**to (or for) the nations**
Acc.	gentem	means	**the nation**	gentēs	means	**the nations**
Abl.	cum gente	means	**with the nation**	cum gentibus	means	**with the nations**

Nominative singular is only one syllable
(with stem ending in two consonants)

Nom.	urbs	means	**the city**	urbēs	means	**the cities**
Gen.	urbis	means	**of the city**	urbium	means	**of the cities**
Dat.	urbī	means	**to (or for) the city**	urbibus	means	**to (or for) the cities**
Acc.	urbem	means	**the city**	urbēs	means	**the cities**
Abl.	in urbe	means	**in the city**	in urbibus	means	**in the cities**

Write the third declension nouns on the right under the correct headings.

"I-Stem"	Not "I-Stem"
_____	_____
_____	_____
_____	_____
_____	_____

avis
clāmor
iūdex
mors

☐ Flashcards - (Add the new cards.)

GRAMMAR REVIEW
Declensions

Neuter Nouns
(Nominative and accusative singular endings are always the same in neuter nouns.)
(Nominative and accusative plural always end in -a in neuter nouns.)

Second Declension Nouns - Neuter
(Genitive singular ends in -ī. Nominative singular ends in -um.)

	Singular			Plural	
Nom.	caelum	means **the sky**	caela	means **the skies**
Gen.	caelī	means **of the sky**	caelōrum	means **of the skies**
Dat.	caelō	means **to (or for) the sky**	caelīs	means **to (or for) the skies**
Acc.	caelum	means **the sky**	caela	means **the skies**
Abl.	in caelō	means **in the sky**	in caelīs	means **in the skies**

Third Declension Nouns - Neuter
(Genitive singular ends in -is.)

	Singular			Plural	
Nom.	nōmen	means **the name**	nōmina	means **the names**
Gen.	nōminis	means **of the name**	nōminum	means **of the names**
Dat.	nōminī	means **to (or for) the name**	nōminibus	means **to (or for) the names**
Acc.	nōmen	means **the name**	nōmina	means **the names**
Abl.	nōmine	means **with the name**	nōminibus	means **with the names**

Third Declension I-Stem Nouns - Neuter
(Genitive singular ends in -is. Nominative singular ends in -al or -e.)
(Ablative singular ends in -ī instead of -e. Nominative and accusative plural end in -ia instead of -ēs.)

	Singular			Plural	
Nom.	mare	means **the sea**	maria	means **the seas**
Gen.	maris	means **of the sea**	marium	means **of the seas**
Dat.	marī	means **to (or for) the sea**	maribus	means **to (or for) the seas**
Acc.	mare	means **the sea**	maria	means **the seas**
Abl.	in marī	means **in the sea**	in maribus	means **in the seas**

Add the correct endings to the Latin nouns.

Accusative Plural	Ablative Singular	Genitive Plural
animāl_____	itiner_____	perīcul_____
gaudi_____	praemi_____	pān_____

☐ Flashcards - (Add the new cards.)

GRAMMAR REVIEW
Present Active Indicative Verbs

Fourth Conjugation Verbs

(Second principal part ends in -īre. Drop -re from the second principal part to find the present stem [audī-].)

	Singular				**Plural**		
1st Person	audiō	means	**I hear.**		audīmus	means	**We hear.**
2nd Person	audīs	means	**You (s.) hear.**		audītis	means	**You (pl.) hear.**
3rd Person	audit	means	**He (she, it) hears.**		audiunt	means	**They hear.**

The "Being" Verb

(Sum has an irregular present stem, but the endings are regular.)
(The principal parts of sum are sum, esse, fuī, and futūrus.)

	Singular				**Plural**		
1st Person	sum	means	**I am.**		sumus	means	**We are.**
2nd Person	es	means	**You (s.) are.**		estis	means	**You (pl.) are.**
3rd Person	est	means	**He (she, it) is, there is.**		sunt	means	**They are, there are.**

Translate these Latin words.

1. The Latin word _____ means **he sleeps**.

2. The Latin word _____ means **there are**.

3. The Latin word _____ means **they come upon**.

4. The Latin word _____ means **she knows**.

5. The Latin word _____ means **you (s.) are**.

6. The Latin word _____ means **you (pl.) discover**.

7. The Latin word _____ means **we are**.

☐ Flashcards - (Add the new cards.)

GRAMMAR REVIEW
Declensions

Fourth Declension Nouns - Masculine and Feminine

(Genitive singular ends in -ūs. Drop the -ūs from the genitive singular to find the stem [man-].)
(Fourth declension nouns are usually masculine, but sometimes feminine or neuter.)

	Singular			Plural		
Nom.	manus	means	**the hand**	manūs	means	**the hands**
Gen.	manūs	means	**of the hand**	manuum	means	**of the hands**
Dat.	manuī	means	**to (or for) the hand**	manibus	means	**to (or for) the hands**
Acc.	manum	means	**the hand**	manūs	means	**the hands**
Abl.	in manū	means	**in the hand**	in manibus	means	**in the hands**

Fourth Declension Nouns - Neuter

(Genitive singular ends in -ūs. The nominative singular of fourth declension neuter nouns ends in -ū.)
(Drop the -ūs from the genitive singular to find the stem [corn-].)

	Singular			Plural		
Nom.	cornū	means	**the horn**	cornua	means	**the horns**
Gen.	cornūs	means	**of the horn**	cornuum	means	**of the horns**
Dat.	cornū	means	**to (or for) the horn**	cornibus	means	**to (or for) the horns**
Acc.	cornū	means	**the horn**	cornua	means	**the horns**
Abl.	cornū	means	**with the horn**	cornibus	means	**with the horns**

Circle all possible cases for the Latin nouns. Circle the genders and declensions.

potestātēs	nom	gen	dat	acc	abl	m	f	n	1st	2nd	3rd	3rd-I	4th
adventum	nom	gen	dat	acc	abl	m	f	n	1st	2nd	3rd	3rd-I	4th
portuī	nom	gen	dat	acc	abl	m	f	n	1st	2nd	3rd	3rd-I	4th
dōnō	nom	gen	dat	acc	abl	m	f	n	1st	2nd	3rd	3rd-I	4th
fluctūs	nom	gen	dat	acc	abl	m	f	n	1st	2nd	3rd	3rd-I	4th
cēnae	nom	gen	dat	acc	abl	m	f	n	1st	2nd	3rd	3rd-I	4th
exitibus	nom	gen	dat	acc	abl	m	f	n	1st	2nd	3rd	3rd-I	4th
avis	nom	gen	dat	acc	abl	m	f	n	1st	2nd	3rd	3rd-I	4th
cornua	nom	gen	dat	acc	abl	m	f	n	1st	2nd	3rd	3rd-I	4th

☐ Flashcards - (Add the new cards.)

GRAMMAR REVIEW
Declensions

Fifth Declension Nouns - Masculine and Feminine

(Recognize this form by the -ēī or eī at the end of the genitive singular.)
(The genitive singular ending is actually -ī. The -ē- [or -e- if after a consonant and before a vowel] is the stem ending.)
(Fifth declension nouns are usually feminine, but sometimes masculine.)

Genitive singular ending in -ēī

	Singular			Plural		
Nom.	diēs	means	**the day**	diēs	means	**the days**
Gen.	diēī	means	**of the day**	diērum	means	**of the days**
Dat.	diēī	means	**to (or for) the day**	diēbus	means	**to (or for) the days**
Acc.	diem	means	**the day**	diēs	means	**the days**
Abl.	diē	means	**by means of the day**	diēbus	means	**by means of the days**

Genitive singular ending in -eī

(The -ē- is shortened to -e- after a consonant and before a vowel.)

	Singular			Plural		
Nom.	spēs	means	**the hope**	spēs	means	**the hopes**
Gen.	speī	means	**of the hope**	spērum	means	**of the hopes**
Dat.	speī	means	**to (or for) the hope**	spēbus	means	**to (or for) the hopes**
Acc.	spem	means	**the hope**	spēs	means	**the hopes**
Abl.	spē	means	**by means of the hope**	spēbus	means	**by means of the hopes**

Finish the words with the correct endings.

1. flōr_____ (the flowers)

2. exit_____ (of the departures)

3. sp_____ (for the hopes)

4. cib_____ (of the food)

5. di_____ (of the day)

6. proeli_____ (the battle)

7. fid_____ (of the pledges)

8. corn_____ (for the horn)

9. sp_____ (of the hope)

10. fluct_____ (for the waves)

11. mēns_____ (of the courses)

12. arbor_____ (of the tree)

☐ Flashcards - (Add the new cards.)

26

GRAMMAR REVIEW
Macrons and Word Order

Macrons

(A macron is a horizontal line placed over a long vowel. Learn macron placement when learning the spelling of a word.)
(The Romans did not use macrons. Latin grammar books often use them to aid in teaching the length of vowels.)
(When pronounced, hold a vowel with a macron twice as long as a vowel without a macron.)

Rules for Macron Placement

1. A vowel **always** has a macron before the letters -ns.
2. A vowel **never** has a macron before the letters -nt.
3. When the vowel -e- comes after another vowel, it has a macron.
4. When an -m, -r, or -t is the last letter in an ending added to a word, the vowel that comes before the -m, -r, or -t is **never** long.
5. If an -m, -r, or -t is the last letter in a word without an ending, the vowel that comes before the -m, -r, or -t is *almost* **never** long. (Exception: cūr)

Cross out the Latin words with incorrectly used or omitted macrons.

prūdens	āmittit	frātrum	ante	tum
tenet	reddunt	trans	dieī	terrēnt
aut	movēō	nam	pēr	cōntrā
arbōr	īnter	fidēī	gēns	potēns

Word Order

(Word order in Latin is not the same as word order in English.)

English	**Latin**
The *position* of the word tells what role the word plays in the sentence.	The *ending* of the word tells what role the word plays in the sentence.
Normal word order: SUBJECT - VERB - DIRECT OBJECT	Normal word order: Most important word (usually the verb) is often *last*. Second most important word is often *first*.

(Note: If the Latin verb is a linking verb, the Latin word order usually follows the English word order.)

☐ Flashcards - (Add the new card.)

GRAMMAR REVIEW
Syllables and Accents

Names of Syllables

The last syllable is the **ultima**, the syllable before the ultima is the **penult**, and the syllable before the penult is the **antepenult**.

e   pis   tu   la
antepenult   penult   ultima

Rules for Length of Syllables

Syllables can be **long by nature** or **long by position**.
Turn to the appendix and review the **Rules for Length of Syllables**.

Circle the correct words.

1. In laetus, lae- is (short, long) and is called the (antepenult, penult, ultima).
2. In dēfessus, dē- is (short, long) and is called the (antepenult, penult, ultima).

Rules for Dividing Syllables

Turn to the appendix and review the four specific **Rules for Dividing Syllables**.

Divide the words correctly by drawing a vertical line between syllables.

magnopere   maximē   ōrātiō   fenestra

Rules of Accent

Turn to the appendix and review the three **Rules of Accent**.

Write **a** beside the words that take an accent on the *antepenult*, **p** beside the words that take an accent on the *penult*, and **u** beside words that take an accent on the *ultima*.

____ 1. perficiō   ____ 2. flōs   ____ 3. āmittō   ____ 4. audācter

☐ Flashcards - (Add the new cards.)

28   Latin Workbook - Level 6
Copyright © 2006 by Karen Mohs

GRAMMAR REVIEW
Connectives and Question Words

***Connectives - The word* et**
(Place et between the words it connects.)

Pater et māter filium amant.
The father **and** the mother love the son.

***Connectives - Enclitic** -que**
(Place -que at the end of the second of the two words it connects.)
(Used with words of like syntax [i.e. both are subjects, both are direct objects, etc.].)

Pater māterque filium amant.
The father **and** the mother love the son.

***Question Words - Expects* Yes or No Answer**
(Add the enclitic* -ne to the end of the first word in the sentence.)
(Used when the answer can be either *yes* or *no*.)

Puellamne laudat?
Does he praise the girl?

The answer? *Yes, he praises the girl* or *No, he does not praise the girl.*

***Question Words - Expects* Yes Answer**
(Use a negative word [usually nōn] with the -ne attached to it at the beginning of the sentence.)

Nōnne puellam laudat?
He praises the girl, doesn't he?

The answer? *Yes, he praises the girl.*

***Question Words - Expects* No Answer**
(Use the word num at the beginning of the sentence.)

Num puellam laudat?
He doesn't praise the girl, does he?

The answer? *No, he does not praise the girl.*

*In Latin, an *enclitic* is a group of letters that must be attached to the end of another word.

☐ Flashcards - (Add the new card.)

GRAMMAR REVIEW
Adjectives

Learning Adjectives

Adjectives in Latin, as in English, are words that modify nouns or pronouns. Latin adjectives agree with the words they modify in gender, number, and case.

That's why, when we learn adjectives, we must learn:

1. Three genders: masculine, feminine, and neuter

2. Both numbers: singular and plural

3. Five cases: nominative, genitive, dative, accusative, ablative

Adjectives
(First and Second Declension)

(Latin adjectives ending in -us, -a, -um are **first and second declension** adjectives.)

	Masculine	Singular Feminine	Neuter	Masculine	Plural Feminine	Neuter
Nom.	bonus	bona	bonum	bonī	bonae	bona
Gen.	bonī	bonae	bonī	bonōrum	bonārum	bonōrum
Dat.	bonō	bonae	bonō	bonīs	bonīs	bonīs
Acc.	bonum	bonam	bonum	bonōs	bonās	bona
Abl.	bonō	bonā	bonō	bonīs	bonīs	bonīs

Substantive Use of Adjectives

In Latin, as in English, a *substantive adjective* is an adjective that is used as a noun.

Latin Substantive	English Meaning	Latin Substantive	English Meaning
bonus	*a good man*	bonī	*good men*
bona	*a good woman*	bonae	*good women*
bonum	*a good thing*	bona	*good things*

☐ Flashcards - (Add the new cards.)

GRAMMAR REVIEW
Adjectives

Adjectives
(First and Second Declension)

(Some Latin **first and second declension** adjectives end in -er.)
(Some of these -er adjectives retain the vowel in the stem.)
(Drop the -a from the feminine singular to find the stem [miser-].)

	Masculine (Singular)	Feminine (Singular)	Neuter (Singular)	Masculine (Plural)	Feminine (Plural)	Neuter (Plural)
Nom.	miser	misera	miserum	miserī	miserae	misera
Gen.	miserī	miserae	miserī	miserōrum	miserārum	miserōrum
Dat.	miserō	miserae	miserō	miserīs	miserīs	miserīs
Acc.	miserum	miseram	miserum	miserōs	miserās	misera
Abl.	miserō	miserā	miserō	miserīs	miserīs	miserīs

(Most of the -er adjectives do not retain the vowel in the stem.)*
(Drop the -a from the feminine singular to find the stem [pulchr-].)

	Masculine (Singular)	Feminine (Singular)	Neuter (Singular)	Masculine (Plural)	Feminine (Plural)	Neuter (Plural)
Nom.	pulcher	pulchra	pulchrum	pulchrī	pulchrae	pulchra
Gen.	pulchrī	pulchrae	pulchrī	pulchrōrum	pulchrārum	pulchrōrum
Dat.	pulchrō	pulchrae	pulchrō	pulchrīs	pulchrīs	pulchrīs
Acc.	pulchrum	pulchram	pulchrum	pulchrōs	pulchrās	pulchra
Abl.	pulchrō	pulchrā	pulchrō	pulchrīs	pulchrīs	pulchrīs

Fill in the chart with the correct adjective endings.

	Masculine	Feminine	Neuter
Genitive Plural	sinistr_____	sinistr_____	sinistr_____
Dative Singular	miser_____	miser_____	miser_____
Accusative Plural	laet_____	laet_____	laet_____

*In the masculine gender, the difference is apparent in the genitive, dative, accusative, and ablative cases of these first and second declension -er adjectives. It is also apparent throughout the feminine and neuter genders.

☐ Flashcards - (Add the new cards.)

GRAMMAR REVIEW

Write the adjectives under the correct headings. Some words may be used several times.

Singular

Masculine Nominative	Feminine Nominative	Neuter Nominative

Masculine Genitive	Feminine Genitive	Neuter Genitive

Masculine Dative	Feminine Dative	Neuter Dative

Masculine Accusative	Feminine Accusative	Neuter Accusative

Masculine Ablative	Feminine Ablative	Neuter Ablative

clārōs
dēfessī
dextrās
laetus
lātārum
longa
magnā
malam
mediō
miserōrum
parvae
sacrīs
validum

Plural

Masculine Nominative	Feminine Nominative	Neuter Nominative

Masculine Genitive	Feminine Genitive	Neuter Genitive

Masculine Dative	Feminine Dative	Neuter Dative

Masculine Accusative	Feminine Accusative	Neuter Accusative

Masculine Ablative	Feminine Ablative	Neuter Ablative

☐ Flashcards

Latin Workbook - Level 6
Copyright © 2006 by Karen Mohs

GRAMMAR REVIEW

Fill in the chart with the correct adjective endings.

	Masculine Singular	Feminine Singular	Neuter Singular	Masculine Plural	Feminine Plural	Neuter Plural
Gen.	laet_____	laet_____	laet_____	laet_____	laet_____	laet_____
Acc.	nostr_____	nostr_____	nostr_____	nostr_____	nostr_____	nostr_____
Dat.	medi_____	medi_____	medi_____	medi_____	medi_____	medi_____
Nom.	lāt_____	lāt_____	lāt_____	lāt_____	lāt_____	lāt_____
Acc.	alt_____	alt_____	alt_____	alt_____	alt_____	alt_____
Gen.	dextr_____	dextr_____	dextr_____	dextr_____	dextr_____	dextr_____
Dat.	long_____	long_____	long_____	long_____	long_____	long_____
Gen.	valid_____	valid_____	valid_____	valid_____	valid_____	valid_____
Abl.	sacr_____	sacr_____	sacr_____	sacr_____	sacr_____	sacr_____
Nom.	clār_____	clār_____	clār_____	clār_____	clār_____	clār_____
Dat.	vestr_____	vestr_____	vestr_____	vestr_____	vestr_____	vestr_____
Abl.	parv_____	parv_____	parv_____	parv_____	parv_____	parv_____

☐ Flashcards

GRAMMAR REVIEW

Connect the Latin nouns to their adjectives and translations.

sorōrum	laetās	of the happy sister
sorōrēs	laetārum	the small chair
soror	parvam	the happy sisters
sorōris	laeta	of the happy sisters
sorōribus	laetae	the happy sister
sellae	parvae	the tall wave
sellam	laetīs	for the happy sisters
sellīs	parvīs	of the tall wave
fluctūs	altī	of the small chair
fluctuum	altō	for the small chairs
fluctum	altum	to the tall wave
fluctuī	nostrō	of our flowers
fluctibus	altōrum	to the tall waves
flōrum	nostrōrum	our flowers
flōrī	altīs	for our flower
flōrem	nostrī	of the tall waves
flōrēs	dēfessī	for the tired doctor
medicī	nostrum	our flower
medicīs	dēfessus	of the tired doctor
medicō	dēfessīs	the tired doctor
medicōrum	dēfessō	for the tired doctors
medicus	dēfessōrum	the great battle
proelia	magnum	for the great battle
proelium	magnīs	of the tired doctors
proeliīs	magnō	for your speeches
proelī	magna	for the great battles
proeliō	tuīs	the great battles
ōrātiō	magnī	of your speech
ōrātiōnibus	tua	your speeches
ōrātiōnēs	tuae	of the great battle
ōrātiōnis	tuās	your speech

☐ Flashcards

Latin Workbook - Level 6
Copyright © 2006 by Karen Mohs

GRAMMAR REVIEW
Adjectives

Third Declension Adjectives - Three Terminations
(Masculine nominative singular ends in -er; feminine nominative singular ends in -is;
neuter nominative singular ends in -e.)

	Singular Masculine	Feminine	Neuter	Plural Masculine	Feminine	Neuter
Nom.	celer	celeris	celere	celerēs	celerēs	celeria
Gen.	celeris	celeris	celeris	celerium	celerium	celerium
Dat.	celerī	celerī	celerī	celeribus	celeribus	celeribus
Acc.	celerem	celerem	celere	celerēs	celerēs	celeria
Abl.	celerī	celerī	celerī	celeribus	celeribus	celeribus

Third Declension Adjectives - Two Terminations
(Masculine and feminine nominative singular end in -is; neuter nominative singular ends in -e.)

	Singular Masculine/Feminine	Neuter	Plural Masculine/Feminine	Neuter
Nom.	omnis	omne	omnēs	omnia
Gen.	omnis	omnis	omnium	omnium
Dat.	omnī	omnī	omnibus	omnibus
Acc.	omnem	omne	omnēs	omnia
Abl.	omnī	omnī	omnibus	omnibus

Third Declension Adjectives - One Termination
(Masculine nominative singular does **not** end in -er or -is.)

	Singular Masculine/Feminine	Neuter	Plural Masculine/Feminine	Neuter
Nom.	potēns	potēns	potentēs	potentia
Gen.	potentis	potentis	potentium	potentium
Dat.	potentī	potentī	potentibus	potentibus
Acc.	potentem	potēns	potentēs	potentia
Abl.	potentī	potentī	potentibus	potentibus

☐ Flashcards - (Add the new cards.)

GRAMMAR REVIEW

Identify the adjectives. In the first column, write **M** (masculine), **F** (feminine), and/or **N** (neuter). In the second, write **Nom** (nominative), **Gen** (genitive), **Dat** (dative), **Acc** (accusative), and/or **Abl** (ablative). In the third column, write **S** (singular) or **P** (plural).

N	____	__	1. omnis		____	____	__	21. brevem
____	____	__	2. similēs		____	____	__	22. fidēlī
____	**Acc**	__	3. dextrum		____	____	__	23. longā
____	____	__	4. ācer		____	____	__	24. fortium
____	____	__	5. facilibus		**F**	____	__	25. ācris
____	____	__	6. trīstium		____	____	**S**	26. vestrae
____	____	__	7. grave		____	____	__	27. omnia
____	**Nom**	__	8. audāx		**N**	____	__	28. prūdēns
____	____	**P**	9. clārae		____	____	__	29. mediās
____	____	__	10. celerēs		____	____	__	30. fēlīcia
____	____	__	11. prūdentis		____	____	__	31. gravibus
____	____	__	12. fortī		____	____	__	32. lātōrum
____	____	__	13. validīs		____	____	__	33. potentēs
M or F	____	__	14. potēns		____	____	__	34. miser
____	____	**P**	15. nostra		____	____	__	35. trīstem
____	____	__	16. pulchrō		____	____	__	36. bonōs
____	____	__	17. fidēlia		____	**Gen**	__	37. similis
____	____	__	18. ācre		____	____	__	38. celeria
____	____	__	19. fēlīcēs		____	____	__	39. facile
____	____	__	20. brevium		____	____	__	40. audācī

☐ Flashcards

GRAMMAR REVIEW

Fill in the chart with the correct adjective endings.

	Masculine Singular	Feminine Singular	Neuter Singular	Masculine Plural	Feminine Plural	Neuter Plural
Dat.	grav_____	grav_____	grav_____	grav_____	grav_____	grav_____
Abl.	mal_____	mal_____	mal_____	mal_____	mal_____	mal_____
Acc.	fidēl_____	fidēl_____	fidēl_____	fidēl_____	fidēl_____	fidēl_____
Gen.	facil_____	facil_____	facil_____	facil_____	facil_____	facil_____
Abl.	fort_____	fort_____	fort_____	fort_____	fort_____	fort_____
Dat.	celer_____	celer_____	celer_____	celer_____	celer_____	celer_____
Acc.	brev_____	brev_____	brev_____	brev_____	brev_____	brev_____
Nom.	ācer_____	ācr_____	ācr_____	ācr_____	ācr_____	ācr_____
Dat.	me_____	me_____	me_____	me_____	me_____	me_____
Gen.	trīst_____	trīst_____	trīst_____	trīst_____	trīst_____	trīst_____
Acc.	mult_____	mult_____	mult_____	mult_____	mult_____	mult_____
Nom.	fēlix_____	fēlix_____	fēlix_____	fēlīc_____	fēlīc_____	fēlīc_____

☐ Flashcards

GRAMMAR REVIEW

Write the Latin adjectives and nouns. Remember the correct position and the need for agreement.*

1. the easy life
   (nominative case)

2. of the bold human being

3. for the grim news

4. of the brief epistles

5. in the middle of the waves

6. a beautiful girl
   (accusative case)

7. for the faithful doctors

8. the tired judges
   (nominative case)

9. of holy words

10. all the brave heroes

11. for the happy hours

12. of the powerful weapons

13. many serious reasons
    (accusative case)

14. the famous poets
    (nominative case)

15. to the wise man

*Exception: When adjectives express quantity, numerals, or are interrogative or emphatic, they often precede the nouns they modify.

☐ Flashcards

GRAMMAR REVIEW
Prepositions

Prepositions and Cases

Review the correct case for the prepositions.

Preposition	Case (of noun following the preposition)	Meaning
ā, ab	ablative case	from, away from, by
ad	accusative case	to, near, toward, for, at
ante	accusative case	before, in front of
contrā	accusative case	against, opposite
cum	ablative case	along with, with
dē	ablative case	down from, from, about, concerning, of
ē, ex	ablative case	out of, from, of
in	accusative case	into, onto, against, toward, for
in	ablative case	in, on, upon, over
inter	accusative case	between, among
ob	accusative case	because of, on account of, for the purpose of
per	accusative case	through, across, by, by means of
post	accusative case	behind, after
sine	ablative case	without
sub	accusative case	close under, under, close to, up to, to the foot of
sub	ablative case	at the foot of, under, close to
super	accusative case	over, above
trāns	accusative case	across, over

Circle the correct cases for the nouns which are used with the Latin prepositions.

sine	**accusative**	**ablative**		ex	**accusative**	**ablative**
ā	**accusative**	**ablative**		super	**accusative**	**ablative**
trāns	**accusative**	**ablative**		cum	**accusative**	**ablative**
dē	**accusative**	**ablative**		inter	**accusative**	**ablative**
per	**accusative**	**ablative**		ante	**accusative**	**ablative**

☐ Flashcards

GRAMMAR REVIEW

Write the prepositions under the correct headings. Some words may be used more than
once. Beside the prepositions, write the possible meanings.

Takes the Ablative Case   Meanings

Takes the Accusative Case   Meanings

ā
ab
ad
ante
contrā
cum
dē
ē
ex
in
inter
ob
per
post
sine
trāns

☐ Flashcards

40   Latin Workbook - Level 6
                                              Copyright © 2006 by Karen Mohs

GRAMMAR REVIEW
Case Uses

Accusative of Place to Which
(To indicate the location that is the goal of the verb's action,
use the prepositions in or ad or sub with the accusative case.)

	Singular	**Plural**
Use with in	In vīllam puella ambulat. The girl walks *into the villa*.	In vīllās puella ambulat. The girl walks *into the villas*.
Use with ad	Ad vīllam puella ambulat. The girl walks *to the villa*.	Ad vīllās puella ambulat. The girl walks *to the villas*.
Use with sub	Sub vīllam puella ambulat. The girl walks *up to the villa*.	Sub vīllās puella ambulat. The girl walks *up to the villas*.

Fill in the blanks with the correct prepositions. Circle the correct cases.

1. Latin _____ means *opposite*. It is used with the (accusative, ablative) case.

2. Latin _____ means *at the foot of*. It is used with the (accusative, ablative) case.

3. Latin _____ means *to*. It is used with the (accusative, ablative) case.

4. Latin _____ means *because of*. It is used with the (accusative, ablative) case.

5. Latin _____ means *into*. It is used with the (accusative, ablative) case.

6. Latin _____ means *with*. It is used with the (accusative, ablative) case.

7. Latin _____ means *up to*. It is used with the (accusative, ablative) case.

8. Latin _____ means *across* or *over*. It is used with the (accusative, ablative) case.

9. Latin _____ means *in front of*. It is used with the (accusative, ablative) case.

10. Latin _____ means *down from*. It is used with the (accusative, ablative) case.

11. Latin _____ means *through*. It is used with the (accusative, ablative) case.

☐ Flashcards - (Add the new cards.)

GRAMMAR REVIEW
Adverbs

About Adverbs

Adverbs in Latin, as in English, modify verbs, adjectives, or other adverbs.

Adverbs from First and Second Declension Adjectives

To form an adverb from a first or second declension adjective, simply add -ē to the stem* of the adjective.

Adjective	Meaning	Adverb	Meaning
altus	high, tall, deep	altē	on high, deeply
miser	unhappy, wretched, unfortunate, poor	miserē	wretchedly, desperately
pulcher	beautiful, noble, fine	pulchrē	beautifully, nobly
lātus	wide, broad	lātē	widely

Some adverbs, however, are irregular and cannot be formed by adding -ē to the stem of the adjective. These irregular adverbs must be learned individually.

Adjective	Meaning	Adverb	Meaning
bonus	good	bene	well, fully
malus	bad, evil	male	badly, insufficiently

Adverbs from Third Declension Adjectives

To form an adverb from a third declension adjective, add -iter (or just -er if the stem ends in -nt-) to the stem* of the adjective.

Adjective	Meaning	Adverb	Meaning
celer	quick, swift, speedy	celeriter	quickly, swiftly
brevis	short, brief	breviter	briefly
ācer	sharp, fierce	ācriter	sharply, fiercely
potēns	powerful	potenter	powerfully

*Remember: To find the stem of an adjective, drop the ending from the feminine singular form of the nominative case. For adjectives of one termination, drop the ending from the genitive singular form.

☐ Flashcards

GRAMMAR REVIEW

In the first column you will see *first and second declension* adjectives. In the second column, write the feminine singular form of these adjectives. In the third column, write the base of the adjectives. In the fourth column, write the adverbs formed from the adjectives.

	Nominative Case Feminine Singular	Base	Adverb
laetus			
medius			
validus			
longus			

Next we convert *third declension adjectives* of **two** or **three terminations** to adverbs.

	Nominative Case Feminine Singular	Base	Adverb
similis			
trīstis			
ācer			
fidēlis			
celer			
gravis			

Finally, we convert a *third declension adjective* of **one termination** to an adverb. Notice that the heading over the second column is now *genitive singular*. Remember that the genitive singular is used to determine the base of third declension adjectives of one termination.

	Genitive Singular	Base	Adverb
fēlix			

☐ Flashcards

PUZZLE TIME

Find twenty Latin words in the puzzle. (Macrons have been omitted.)

```
u b i e i q n q d x p y l s z b a p c k v s t a t i m
q s b s x t n v z s q d p e r f i c i o q n v d k t s
n v i h m q u r y p n f v s g r g s b v q c b h v a h
r d z k a o m a g n o p e r e m d c u x v o z u u q d
g c y z i s q z a r n l v m t v n x s z m n t c q u v
p r a e m i u m y v d v m f i f q s x y l s q i u e e
o q x l v z a u s z u n q f a c i l i s z t n k q q h
t t m a x i m e a o m q a q m o q k p e r i c u l u m
e k n u y l d h k l y p k z f v r t k z v t k g c f v
n z p t s d f d e f e s s u s n x p q l r u i b d b r
s k n l z s t r q t z a t h s n e q u e q o l q s s p
```

Write the words you found, adding macrons where needed.

1. _____   11. _____

2. _____   12. _____

3. _____   13. _____

4. _____   14. _____

5. _____   15. _____

6. _____   16. _____

7. _____   17. _____

8. _____   18. _____

9. _____   19. _____

10. _____   20. _____

☐ Flashcards

44

līber lībera līberum (adjective) means free līberī (līberōrum) means **children**	mox (adverb) means soon
rēgnō rēgnāre rēgnāvī rēgnātum means reign, dominate, rule	carmen carminis (n.) means song, poem

Write the Latin words. (When more than one Latin word fits the definition, use the most recent word learned.)

not yet _____   at once _____

soon _____   never _____

children _____   greatly _____

song _____

snatch _____

joyful _____

tired _____

reign _____

free _____

☐ Flashcards - (Add the new cards.)

LET'S PRACTICE

Match the words to their meanings.

mox	death
carrus	wagon
carmen	soon
mors	poem
līberō	book
liber	free
līber	I set free
rēgnō	queen
reddō	I rule
rēgis	I restore
rēgīna	of the king

Read the Latin sentences and translate.

1. Rēx dēfessus est, sed tamen* diū rēgnat in terrā hostium.

   It means _____

2. Quā dē causā medicī multa carmina nārrant, et puerī mox dormiunt.

   It means _____

3. Sed interim in pulchrō rēgīnae hortō** līberōs laetōs vidēmus

   It means _____

4. Quōmodo homō malus ex agrō parvam puellam prūdentem*** celeriter rapit?

   It means _____

*This word is postpositive, which means it cannot occur first in its clause. It usually is the second word.

**When an adjective and a genitive modify a noun, the usual order is adjective - genitive - noun.

***If two adjectives modify a noun, the usual order is adjective - noun - adjective. (If one of the adjectives is possessive, such as meus or tuus, that possessive adjective is usually the one placed after the noun.)

☐ Flashcards

Latin Workbook - Level 6
Copyright © 2006 by Karen Mohs

summus	novus
summa summum	**nova novum**
(adjective)	(adjective)
means	means
highest, top of, greatest, chief	new
summē (adverb) means **very, intensely, extremely**	novē (adverb) means **newly**

flūmen	dum
flūminis (n.)	(conjunction)
means	means
flowing, river, stream	while, until, as long as

Write the Latin words. (When more than one Latin word fits the definition, use the most recent word learned.)

while _____ soon _____

flowing _____ children _____

newly _____ very _____

free _____

highest _____

dominate _____

poem _____

new _____

foresighted _____

☐ Flashcards - (Add the new cards.)

Latin Workbook - Level 6
Copyright © 2006 by Karen Mohs

LET'S PRACTICE

Match the words to their meanings.

fidēs	flower
flōs	faith
flūmen	happy
fēlix	river
dōnum	present
dux	guide
dum	until
summē	top of
novus	newly
novē	new
summus	intensely

Read the Latin sentences and translate.

1. Dum pater trīstis surgit et fābulam nārrat, māter audāx pānem rapit.

   It means _____

2. Avis clāmōrēs magistrōrum novōrum audit et in arborēs celeriter volat.

   It means _____

3. In mediōs hortōs* iūdicis validī multā nocte numquam currō.

   It means _____

4. Nāvēs longās vidētis, et in flūmine sine spē miserē nāvigātis.

   It means _____

5. Ā summō mūrō* lēgātōs fortēs in campō lātō vidēmus.

   It means _____

*The adjective medius contains the idea *of* and is not used with a genitive. This is usually true of summus as well.

☐ Flashcards

Latin Workbook - Level 6
Copyright © 2006 by Karen Mohs

iuvō
iuvāre iūvī iūtum*

means

help, do good to, favor

plēnus
plēna plēnum
(adjective)
means

full

plēnē (adverb) means **fully, completely**

grātus
grāta grātum
(adjective)
means

pleasing, welcome, thankful

grātē (adverb) means **gratefully, pleasantly, willingly**

iniūria
iniūriae (f.)

means

injustice, insult, injury

Write the Latin words. (When more than one Latin word fits the definition, use the most recent word learned.)

river _____

children _____

fully _____

reign _____

new _____

help _____

pleasing _____

full _____

greatest _____

until _____

injustice _____

gratefully _____

*Notice and learn the irregular principal parts of this first conjugation verb.

☐ Flashcards - (Add the new cards.)

LET'S PRACTICE

Match the words to their meanings.

grātē	pleasantly
plēnus	welcome
grātus	completely
plēnē	full
iūdex	I do good to
iuvō	I consider
iūdicō	juror
iniūria	poverty
iānua	insult
inopia	island
īnsula	door

Read the Latin sentences and translate.

1. Es frātrī nostrō grātus, sed frāter noster magistrō nōn grātus*.

   It means _____

2. Fīliae nautārum in mēnsā cēnam grātē pōnunt et ad fenestram sedent.

   It means _____

3. Post rēgis iniūriās nūntiī senātuī poenam nūntiant.

   It means _____

4. Caelum ergō est plēnum carminum laetōrum avium multārum et pulchrārum.

   It means _____

5. Cūr virōs ā sinistrō cornū iuvās, sed in oppidō ducēs summē pugnās?

   It means _____

*In a sentence with parallel clauses, one verb is sometimes omitted when it can be supplied from context.

☐ Flashcards

cōgō cōgere coēgī coāctum* means collect, compel	**vōx** vōcis (f.) means voice
prohibeō prohibēre prohibuī prohibitum* means prevent, hold back, keep ... from	**iubeō** iubēre iussī iussum* means order, command, bid

Write the Latin words. (When more than one Latin word fits the definition, use the most recent word learned.)

injury _____   voice _____

full _____

prevent _____

thankful _____

chief _____

order _____

favor _____

collect _____

*The verb iubeō *must* be used with an infinitive (see page 57) which has a subject in the accusative case. The verbs cōgō and prohibeō *may* be used with an infinitive which has a subject in the accusative case.

☐ Flashcards - (Add the new cards.)

LET'S PRACTICE

Match the words to their meanings.

iuvō		I throw	
iniūria		I help	
iubeō		insult	
iaciō		I command	
vōx		hero	
via		street	
vir		voice	
cōgō		I hold back	
cēdō		wisely	
prohibeō		I withdraw	
prūdenter		I compel	

Read the Latin sentences and translate.

1. Vōx agricolae puerum terret, et ad vīllam celeriter currit.

   It means _____

2. Prohibeō animālia vestra ā mūrīs urbis nostrī, sed equōs nostrōs oppugnant.

   It means _____

3. Simul atque patrēs nostrī oppidum relinquunt, fēminās līberōsque dēfendimus.

   It means _____

4. Sociī cibum cum dīligentiā cōgunt et captīvīs pānem dant.

   It means _____

5. Soror rēgīnae virum reperit, et rēx diem fēliciter cōnstituit.

   It means _____

☐ Flashcards

Latin Workbook - Level 6
Copyright © 2006 by Karen Mohs

dēbeō*

dēbēre dēbuī dēbitum

means

owe, ought

grātiam dēbeō means **I am under an obligation**

vērus

vēra vērum

(adjective)

means

true

vērē (adverb) means **really, truly**

possum*

posse potuī

means

can, be able

bellum

bellī (n.)

means

war

Write the Latin words. (When more than one Latin word fits the definition, use the most recent word learned.)

voice _____

really _____

order _____

collect _____

hold back _____

owe _____

can _____

true _____

war _____

am under an obligation _____

*The verbs dēbeō and possum need infinitives (see page 57) to complete their meanings. Notice that possum does not have a fourth principal part.

☐ Flashcards - (Add the new cards.)

LET'S PRACTICE

Match the words to their meanings.

posteā	I am able to
bene	fully
possum	war
bellum	afterward
grātiam dēbeō	I am under an obligation
bellum gerō	I give thanks
grātiās agō	I wage war
vērus	true
dēbeō	I owe
vērē	as long as
dum	truly

Read the Latin sentences and translate.

1. Rēx dēfessus bellum cum multīs sociīs contrā hostēs patriae nostrae gerit.

   It means _____

2. Flōrēs carminaque vērē amāmus, sed grātiam rēgīnae malae dēbēmus.*

   It means _____

3. Interim per silvam ambulās et inter arborēs diū sedēs.

   It means _____

4. Fīliī vestrī nōn sōlum nautae audācēs prūdentēsque sed etiam amīcī vērī sunt.

   It means _____

5. Animī fēminārum captīvōrum vēritātem verbōrum sorōris meae plēnē dēmōnstrant.

   It means _____

*The idiom grātiam dēbeō is used with the dative of the person.

☐ Flashcards

Latin Workbook - Level 6
Copyright © 2006 by Karen Mohs

LET'S PRACTICE

Translate these sentences into Latin.

1. Therefore, you (singular) see the large waves and sail into the harbor.

   -
   _____

2. We do not seize the strong lieutenant with boldness.

   -
   _____

3. The brave guide leads the family without hope out of danger.

   -
   _____

4. In a short time, the lucky children hold the new books.

   -
   _____

5. We run into the little farmhouse and stay there.

   -
   _____

6. I stand near the river and write with anger about the injustice.

   -
   _____

7. What does our father now say to the chief poet?

   -
   _____

8. The messenger is happy because he eats dessert.

   -
   _____

9. You (plural) gladly see the garden full of beautiful flowers.

   -
   _____

10. Does the king always rule the people with a heavy hand?

    -
    _____

☐ Flashcards

TRANSLATION

Fill in the missing words from the list on the column. Macrons have been omitted.

always faithful

_____

(Motto: US Marine Corps)

God is the chief good.

_____

Fortune favors the brave.

_____

(Virgil)

Behold the man!

_____

(Pilate - John 19:5)

anno
audaces
bonum
dei
deus
domini
dum
ecce
est
est
est
fidelis
fortuna
homo
iuvat
omnia
plena
populus
regnat
semper
spes
summum
sunt
vita

The people rule.

_____

(State Motto: AR)

*While there is life,
there is hope.*

_____

(Cicero)

*All things are
full of God.*

_____

in the year of our Lord

_____

☐ Flashcards

INFINITIVES

What Are Infinitives?

An infinitive is a verbal noun. This means that an infinitive acts in some ways like a *noun* (it can function as a subject or as an object), but it is also like a *verb* (it has tense and voice).*

The *present* infinitive is the second principal part of the Latin verb. (See page 15.)

Subjective Infinitive
(an infinitive acting as a subject)
Vidēre est scīre.   **To see** is to know.

Complementary Infinitive
(an infinitive acting as an object - required by certain verbs to complete their meaning)
Cupit edere.   He wants **to eat**.

(Verbs such as parō, cupiō, cōnstituō, temptō, dēbeō, possum, and prohibeō may require an infinitive to complete their meaning.)

Objective Infinitive
(an infinitive acting as an object with its subject in the accusative case)
Iubet virōs edere.   He orders **the men to eat**.

(Certain verbs such as iubeō, cōgō, and prohibeō are commonly used with the objective infinitive.)

Indirect Statement
(an infinitive with a subject in the accusative case used to report something indirectly)
(used after verbs of saying, thinking, knowing, and perceiving)

Statement Puer edit.   The boy eats.
Indirectly Reported Vir dīcit puerum edere.   The man says that the boy eats.

(*Saying* verbs include dīcō, nūntiō, nārrō, scrībō, doceō, dēmōnstrō, and moneō.)
(*Knowing* verbs include sciō and memoriā teneō.)
(*Thinking* verbs include habeō.)
(*Perceiving* and *feeling* verbs include videō and audiō.)
(Other verbs included in these categories will be learned later.)

*The three tenses of Latin infinitives: present, future, and perfect.

☐ Flashcards - (Add the new cards.)

LET'S PRACTICE

Read the Latin sentences and translate. Circle the use of the infinitive in the sentences.

1. Pater meus iubet poētās trīstēs epistulās dē morte socī scrībere.

   It means _____

   Circle: subjective | complementary | objective | indirect statement

2. Dum temptātis verba memoriā tenēre, equōs vestrōs ante portam vidētis.

   It means _____

   Circle: subjective | complementary | objective | indirect statement

3. Sciō līberōs pulchra avium in arbore carmina audīre.

   It means _____

   Circle: subjective | complementary | objective | indirect statement

4. Sedēre in hortō cum multīs flōribus est vītam bonam laetamque scīre.

   It means _____

   Circle: subjective | complementary | objective | indirect statement

5. Interim prohibēs gentēs lapidēs in fenestram iacere.

   It means _____

   Circle: subjective | complementary | objective | indirect statement

6. Lēgātus scrībit multōs medicōs in urbe novā fēlīciter nōn habitāre.

   It means _____

   Circle: subjective | complementary | objective | indirect statement

7. Cupimus saepe per silvam cum parvīs frātribus nostrīs multā nocte ambulāre.

   It means _____

   Circle: subjective | complementary | objective | indirect statement

☐ Flashcards

caput	propter
capitis (n.)	(preposition - used with the accusative case)
means	means
head	because of, on account of
ignis	**grātia**
ignis (m.)	grātiae (f.)
means	means
fire	gratitude, influence, favor
	grātiam habeō means **I feel gratitude**

Write the Latin words. (When more than one Latin word fits the definition, use the most recent word learned.)

gratitude _____

war _____

feel gratitude _____

head _____

true _____

am able _____

compel _____

ought _____

bid _____

fire _____

because of _____

am under an obligation _____

voice _____

☐ Flashcards - (Add the new cards.)

LET'S PRACTICE

Match the words to their meanings.

grātiam dēbeō	I am under an obligation
quā dē causā	for which reason
grātiās agō	I feel gratitude
grātiam habeō	I give thanks
grātia	serious
grātus	influence
gravis	welcome
ignis	I take
propter	head
caput	on account of
capiō	fire

Read the Latin sentences and translate.

1. Senātūs nostrī monent omnēs puerōs ignem in vīllā nostrā numquam relinquere.

   It means _____

2. Prūdēns pater tuus iubet frātrem tuum grātiam dēfessae mātrī tuae habēre.*

   It means _____

3. Propter fluctūs in marī, līberī in silvā ad multam noctem manent.

   It means _____

4. Dēbēmus grātiās ducibus validīs et cōpiīs fortibus patriae nostrae agere.

   It means _____

5. Cūr servus trīstis flōrēs in capite equī fidēlis saepe iacit?

   It means _____

*The idiom grātiam habeō is used with the dative of the person.

☐ Flashcards

Latin Workbook - Level 6
Copyright © 2006 by Karen Mohs

tempus temporis (n.) means time	**audeō*** audēre ausus sum means dare
amīcus amīca amīcum (adjective) means friendly amīcē (adverb) means **in a friendly way**	**nāvis** nāvis (f.) means ship

Write the Latin words. (When more than one Latin word fits the definition, use the most recent word learned.)

because of _____

fire _____

in a friendly way _____

can _____

dare _____

owe _____

friendly _____

time _____

ship _____

head _____

influence _____

*A *deponent* verb has passive forms, but active meanings. (Passive forms are introduced on page 109.) Audeō has active forms in the present system, but passive forms (ausus sum) in the perfect system. Hence, it is a *semi-deponent* verb. As is true of deponent verbs as well, semi-deponent verbs do not have a fourth principal part.

☐ Flashcards - (Add the new cards.)

LET'S PRACTICE

Match the words to their meanings.

audeō	friendly
audiō	I hear
amīcus	in a friendly way
amīcē	I dare
temptō	I try
tempus	I hold
teneō	time
nauta	battleship
nāvis longa	ship
nāvis	I sail
nāvigō	sailor

Read the Latin sentences and translate.

1. Altus magister noster puerum dēfessum videt, sed scit tempus nōn est dormīre.

   It means _____

2. Hominēs semper amīcī sunt quod carmina avium in hortō audiunt.

   It means _____

3. Ducēs malī prohibent multās nāvēs cibum ad urbēs portāre.

   It means _____

4. Post īram agricolae audiō, per agrōs currere nōn audeō.

   It means _____

5. Itaque miser nūntius noster equōs rēgīnae reperīre numquam potest.*

   It means _____

*The verb potest is the third person singular form of possum. Turn to the appendix and learn all six present tense forms.

☐ Flashcards

62

parātus
parāta parātum
(adjective)
means
ready, prepared
parātē (adverb) means **carefully, promptly, readily**

licet
(impersonal verb* - used with the dative case)

means
it is permitted

oportet
(impersonal verb* - used with the accusative case)

means
it is necessary, it is proper

iūs
iūris (n.)

means
right, law, justice

Write the Latin words. (When more than one Latin word fits the definition, use the most recent word learned.)

right _____

because of _____

ship _____

influence _____

friendly _____

time _____

ready _____

dare _____

ought _____

it is necessary _____

carefully _____

it is permitted _____

fire _____

*The subject of an impersonal verb can be "it," "one," or an infinitive (including an infinitive phrase or clause).

☐ Flashcards - (Add the new cards.)

LET'S PRACTICE

Match the words to their meanings.

parō	prepared
parātē	promptly
parātus	I prepare
parvus	little
licet	free
līber	it is proper
oportet	it is permitted
iubeō	I bid
iuvō	I help
iniūria	law
iūs	injury

Read the Latin sentences and translate.

1. Oportet sorōrēs statim surgere et per iānuam parātē ambulāre.

   It means _____

2. Bonus iūdex noster iūra captīvōrum in viīs oppidī amīcē nūntiat.

   It means _____

3. Nautae parātī nāvem longam in perīculum in fluctibus in marī nāvigant.

   It means _____

4. Parvae avī tuae per fenestram volāre et pānem edere nōn licet.*

   It means _____

5. Puella trīstis rēgī potentī nārrat nāvēs in flūminibus saepe nāvigāre.

   It means _____

*Although impersonal verbs have subjects such as "it," "one," or an infinitive, translate into smooth English if possible.

☐ Flashcards

aestās aestātis (f.) means summer	**gubernō** gubernāre gubernāvī gubernātum means steer, navigate, govern
fugiō fugere fūgī fugitum means flee, flee from, avoid	**hiems** hiemis (f.) means winter

Write the Latin words. (When more than one Latin word fits the definition, use the most recent word learned.)

winter _____

favor _____

it is proper _____

friendly _____

time _____

flee _____

steer _____

prepared _____

dare _____

law _____

it is permitted _____

summer _____

☐ Flashcards - (Add the new cards.)

LET'S PRACTICE

Match the words to their meanings.

fluctus	I flee from
fugiō	flowing
fuga	wave
flūmen	exile
hiems	enemy
herī	winter
hostis	yesterday
gubernō	gladness
ācriter	fiercely
gaudium	summer
aestās	I navigate

Read the Latin sentences and translate.

1. Nauta fortis nāvem per fluctūs altōs in mediō marī gubernat.

   It means _____

2. Hiems est gravis et puerōs nōn dēlectat post omnēs lūdōs aestātis.

   It means _____

3. Aestās est tempus in agrīs labōrāre et nāvēs parvās in flūmine nāvigāre.

   It means _____

4. Līberī agricolārum memoriā tenent captīvōs ā perīculō prūdenter fugere.

   It means _____

5. Puellae pulchrae cupiunt in sellīs ad mēnsam sedēre et secundam mēnsam edere.

   It means _____

☐ Flashcards

66

volō* velle voluī means wish, want, be willing	nōlō nōlle nōluī means not wish, be unwilling
incipiō incipere incēpī inceptum means begin	cīvis cīvis (m. or f.) means citizen

Write the Latin words. (When more than one Latin word fits the definition, use the most recent word learned.)

citizen _____   wish _____

it is
permitted _____   summer _____

justice _____   not wish _____

it is
necessary _____   winter _____

navigate _____

begin _____

ready _____

flee from _____

*Previously, you have learned that volō, volāre, volāvī, volātum means *I fly*. Now you learn an entirely new verb whose first principal part is also volō. Notice the difference in the second and third principal parts of this new verb. Also notice that this new verb does not have a fourth principal part.

☐ Flashcards - (Add the new cards.)

LET'S PRACTICE

Match the words to their meanings.

inopia   need

interficiō   I kill

inveniō   I find

incipiō   I begin

cibus   dinner

cīvis   citizen

cēna   food

volō   I call

nōmen   name

nōlō   I am unwilling

vocō   I am willing

Read the Latin sentences and translate.

1. Magister noster incipit carmina avium audīre, sed carmina nōn amat.

   It means _____

2. Volō* in lectō sorōris meae dormīre, nam cum medicō bonō est.

   It means _____

3. Fēmina ducis fābulās vērās multīs cīvibus urbium nostrārum dē pecūniā rēgis nārrat.

   It means _____

4. Quā dē causā equōs frātrum vestrōrum rapitis et ad silvam fugitis?

   It means _____

5. Nōlō cum animālibus in vīllā parvā in oppidō tuō habitāre.

   It means _____

*The verbs volō and nōlō have irregular forms. Turn to the appendix and learn all six present tense forms of these two verbs.

☐ Flashcards

LET'S PRACTICE

Translate these sentences into Latin.

1. The mothers say that the children run.

2. I am willing that the daughters* see the beautiful flowers in my garden.

3. The son is permitted to write the story near the river.

4. The tired citizen (m.) tries to fight with a sword.

5. We dare to listen to the songs of the evil queen.

6. The birds hear the shouts and fly to the trees.

7. Our leader orders the sailors to steer the ship.

8. I am unwilling that the leader* wound the father's faithful slave.

9. To love is the greatest joy.

10. It is proper for the farmers to sleep briefly in the fields.

*When an infinitive is used with the impersonal verbs volō and nōlō, the subject of the infinitive must be in the accusative case.

☐ Flashcards

TRANSLATION

Fill in the missing words from the list on the column. Macrons have been omitted.

faithful to God and king

_____ _____ _____ _____

_____ _____

We dare to defend our rights.

_____ _____ _____ _____

_____.

(State Motto: AL)

---

the voice of the people

_____ _____ _____

(Alcuin)

---

anew

_____ _____

Column word list:

audemus
audere
de
defendere
deo
deus
est
et
facere
fidelis
fugit
gubernat
in
iura
multum
navem
nostra
novo
parvo
populi
regi
tempus
vox

To dare is to do.

_____ _____ _____.

(Motto: Tottenham Hotspur)

God steers the ship.

_____ _____ _____.

(Motto: Renfrew, Scotland)

Time flees.

_____ _____.

(Virgil)

---

much in little

_____ _____ _____

(Motto: Rutland, England)

☐ Flashcards

PRONOUNS

First and Second Person Pronouns - Singular and Plural

A pronoun is a word that takes the place of a noun.

	1st Person - Singular	Meaning		2nd Person - Singular	Meaning
Nom.	ego*	I		tū*	you (s.)
Gen.	meī**	of me		tuī**	of you (s.)
Dat.	mihi	to/for me		tibi	to/for you (s.)
Acc.	mē	me		tē	you (s.)
Abl.	mē	with/by/from me		tē	with/by/from you (s.)

	1st Person - Plural	Meaning		2nd Person - Plural	Meaning
Nom.	nōs*	we		vōs*	you (pl.)
Gen.	nostrī** or nostrum**	of us		vestrī** or vestrum**	of you (pl.)
Dat.	nōbīs	to/for us		vōbīs	to/for you (pl.)
Acc.	nōs	us		vōs	you (pl.)
Abl.	nōbīs	with/by/from us		vōbīs	with/by/from you (pl.)

Match the personal pronouns to their meanings.

nōs	to us	tū	I
vōbīs	us	mihi	for me
vōs	for you (pl.)	ego	to you (s.)
nōbīs	you (pl.)	tibi	you (s.)

*The pronoun *nominative case* is used for emphasis. Otherwise, the understood pronoun within the verb is all that is needed.

**To express *possession*, the possessive adjective (meus, tuus in the singular and noster, vester in the plural) is used instead of the genitive case of the personal pronoun (meī, tuī in the singular and nostrī/nostrum, vestrī/vestrum in the plural). The genitive case of first and second person pronouns is used in other constructions. (See page 93.)

☐ Flashcards - (Add the new cards.)

LET'S PRACTICE

Circle the correct meanings.

tē	to you (s.) you (s.) for you (s.)	nostrī	of us for us with us
meī	me of me to me	vōbīs	you (pl.) of you (pl.) with you (pl.)
nōs	for us of us we	mē	with me me of me
vestrum	of you (pl.) for you (pl.) with you (pl.)	tuī	you (pl.) by you (s.) of you (s.)

Write the sentences using the words in the box.

1. _____

   It means **Our children run toward us.**

2. _____

   It means **You** (pl.) **hand over our carts to us.**

3. _____

   It means **The physician gives the reward to me.**

4. _____

   It means **The farmer's birds frighten me.**

5. _____

   It means **I** (emphasized) **throw the stone to you** (s.)**.**

ad agricolae avēs carrōs currunt dat ego iaciō lapidem līberī mē medicus mihi nōbīs nōs nostrī nostrōs praemium terrent tibi trāditis

☐ Flashcards

Latin Workbook - Level 6
Copyright © 2006 by Karen Mohs

PRONOUNS

Third Person (Demonstrative) Pronouns - Singular and Plural

Latin uses demonstrative pronouns to act as third person personal pronouns.

	Masculine - Singular	Meaning		Masculine - Plural	Meaning
Nom.	is	he		eī or iī	they
Gen.	eius	of him (his)		eōrum	of them (their)
Dat.	eī	to/for him		eīs	to/for them
Acc.	eum	him		eōs	them
Abl.	eō	with/by/from him		eīs	with/by/from them

	Feminine - Singular	Meaning		Feminine - Plural	Meaning
Nom.	ea	she		eae	they
Gen.	eius	of her (her)		eārum	of them (their)
Dat.	eī	to/for her		eīs	to/for them
Acc.	eam	her		eās	them
Abl.	eā	with/by/from her		eīs	with/by/from them

	Neuter - Singular	Meaning		Neuter - Plural	Meaning
Nom.	id	it		ea	they
Gen.	eius	of it (its)		eōrum	of them (their)
Dat.	eī	to/for it		eīs	to/for them
Acc.	id	it		ea	them
Abl.	eō	with/by/from it		eīs	with/by/from them

Circle first person, box second person, and underline third person pronouns.

nōs   tuī   eae   vestrī   mihi   tū   ea   eōs   ego   nōbīs   eius   vōbīs

☐ Flashcards - (Add the new cards.)

LET'S PRACTICE

Choose the correct words for the sentences, write them in the blanks, and translate.

| eārum - eae | 1. Sorōrēs meae amant fābulās _____ in hortō nārrāre. |

It means _____

| tibi - tū | 2. Ego* et _____ semper cupimus in īnsulā parvā habitāre. |

It means _____

| eius - id | 3. Puer numquam dīcit puellam _____ eīs trādere. |

It means _____

| eam - eā | 4. Pater tuus mātrem tuam videt et cum _____ ambulat. |

It means _____

| tibi - vōs | 5. Servī nostrī dōna celeriter mihi* et _____ et eī dant. |

It means _____

| is - nostrum | 6. Ego* et _____ epistulam nautae trīstī mittimus. |

It means _____

| eum - eius | 7. Rēx _____ gladiōs proeliō multō diē prūdenter parat. |

It means _____

| tuī - tū | 8. _____ et ea* clāmōrēs līberōrum in silvā audītis. |

It means _____

*Unlike the "polite I" in English, Latin places the first person first, the second person second, and the third person third.

☐ Flashcards

74

PRONOUNS

Use of Pronouns

Pronouns in Latin, as in English, are words that take the place of nouns. The word the pronoun stands for is called its *antecedent*.

Example: The son sees the bread and eats it.

antecedent   pronoun

In Latin, a pronoun must agree with its antecedent in *gender* and *number*.

Examples: Lūdum nostrum videō et eum sciō.

masculine singular antecedent   masculine singular pronoun

It means   I see our school and I know it.

(Notice: Although we must use the masculine pronoun eum in Latin, we translate into English using the neuter pronoun *it*.)

Vīllam nostram videō et eam sciō.

feminine singular antecedent   feminine singular pronoun

It means   I see our farmhouse and I know it.

(Notice: Although we must use the feminine pronoun eam in Latin, we translate into English using the neuter pronoun *it*.)

The case of a Latin pronoun is determined by its use in the sentence.

When using cum with a first or second person pronoun as an *ablative of accompaniment*, the cum is attached to the end of the ablative pronoun.

mēcum   tēcum   nōbīscum   vōbīscum

If a third person (demonstrative) pronoun is used with a noun, it is acting as a demonstrative. It should be translated *this* (plural: *these*) or *that* (plural: *those*).

Example: Is est prūdēns.   **It means**   He is wise.

Is puer est prūdēns.   **It means**   This (that) boy is wise.

Latin often omits the possessive pronoun (unless it is needed for emphasis or for clarity). When translating into English, the omitted pronoun should be added.

Example: Patriam dēfendit.   **It means**   He defends ***his*** native land.

Possession is expressed in third person (demonstrative) pronouns by the *genitive case*. This is in contrast to the first and second person in which possession is expressed by the *possessive adjective*. (See second footnote on page 71.)

☐ Flashcards

LET'S PRACTICE

In the first column, write **1st-S** (1st person singular), **1st-P** (1st person plural), **2nd-S** (2nd person singular), **2nd-P** (2nd person plural), **3rd-S-M** (3rd person singular masculine), **3rd-P-M** (3rd person plural masculine), **3rd-S-F** (3rd person singular feminine), **3rd-P-F** (3rd person plural feminine), **3rd-S-N** (3rd person singular neuter), or **3rd-P-N** (3rd person plural neuter). In the second column, write **Nom** (nominative), **Gen** (genitive), **Dat** (dative), **Acc** (accusative), and/or **Abl** (ablative).

_____	_____	1. eō	_____	_____	18. tē
_____	_____	2. nōs	_____	_____	19. eīs
_____	_____	3. is	_____	_____	20. vōs
_____	_____	4. tibi	_____	**Dat**	21. eī
3rd - P - N	_____	5. ea	_____	_____	22. eā
_____	_____	6. vōbīs	_____	_____	23. meī
_____	_____	7. eōs	_____	_____	24. iī
_____	_____	8. ego	_____	_____	25. eōrum
_____	_____	9. eam	_____	_____	26. nostrī
_____	**Nom**	10. eī	_____	_____	27. id
_____	_____	11. tū	**3rd - S - F**	_____	28. ea
_____	_____	12. eius	_____	_____	29. mē
_____	_____	13. eae	_____	_____	30. vestrum
_____	_____	14. nostrum	_____	_____	31. eum
_____	_____	15. eārum	_____	_____	32. eās
_____	_____	16. mihi	_____	_____	33. tuī
_____	_____	17. vestrī	_____	_____	34. nōbīs

☐ Flashcards

NUMERALS

Cardinal Numerals

Cardinal numerals are the most common numerals in Latin.

1 (I) - ūnus, ūna, ūnum	9 (IX) - novem	17 (XVII) - septendecim
2 (II) - duo, duae, duo	10 (X) - decem	18 (XVIII) - duodēvīgintī*
3 (III) - trēs, tria	11 (XI) - ūndecim	19 (XIX) - ūndēvīgintī*
4 (IV) - quattuor	12 (XII) - duodecim	20 (XX) - vīgintī
5 (V) - quīnque	13 (XIII) - tredecim	
6 (VI) - sex	14 (XIV) - quattuordecim	
7 (VII) - septem	15 (XV) - quīndecim	100 (C) - centum
8 (VIII) - octō	16 (XVI) - sēdecim	1000 (M) - mīlle

Declension of Cardinal Numerals

Latin cardinal numerals from *one* to *three* are declined as shown below. The numerals from *four* through *one hundred* are **indeclinable**. That is, the forms do not change to indicate gender, number, and case.

One - ūnus

	Masculine	Feminine	Neuter
Nom.	ūnus	ūna	ūnum
Gen.	ūnīus	ūnīus	ūnīus
Dat.	ūnī	ūnī	ūnī
Acc.	ūnum	ūnam	ūnum
Abl.	ūnō	ūnā	ūnō

Two - duo

	Masculine	Feminine	Neuter
Nom.	duo	duae	duo
Gen.	duōrum	duārum	duōrum
Dat.	duōbus	duābus	duōbus
Acc.	duōs	duās	duo
Abl.	duōbus	duābus	duōbus

Three - trēs

	Masc/Fem	Neuter
Nom.	trēs	tria
Gen.	trium	trium
Dat.	tribus	tribus
Acc.	trēs	tria
Abl.	tribus	tribus

Write the names of the cardinal numerals beside the Roman numerals.

X _____   C _____   V _____   IX _____

*Whereas the Latin numerals from 11 to 17 are formed by addition, the Latin numerals 18 and 19 are formed by subtraction.

☐ Flashcards - (Add the new cards.)

LET'S PRACTICE

Write the correct Latin numerals and their meanings.

ūnus

	Masculine	Feminine	Neuter	Meaning
Nom.				
Gen.				
Dat.				
Acc.				
Abl.				

duo

	Masculine	Feminine	Neuter	Meaning
Nom.				
Gen.				
Dat.				
Acc.				
Abl.				

trēs

	Masculine and Feminine	Neuter	Meaning
Nom.			
Gen.			
Dat.			
Acc.			
Abl.			

☐ Flashcards

NUMERALS

Ordinal Numerals

Ordinal numerals express a position in a sequence.

1st - prīmus, prīma, prīmum
2nd - secundus, -a, -um
3rd - tertius, -a, -um
4th - quārtus, -a, -um
5th - quīntus, -a, -um
6th - sextus, -a, -um
7th - septimus, -a, -um
8th - octāvus, -a, -um
9th - nōnus, -a, -um
10th - decimus, -a, -um

11th - ūndecimus, -a, -um
12th - duodecimus, -a, -um
13th - tertius, -a, -um decimus, -a, -um
14th - quārtus, -a, -um decimus, -a, -um
15th - quīntus, -a, -um decimus, -a, -um
16th - sextus, -a, -um decimus, -a, -um
17th - septimus, -a, -um decimus, -a, -um
18th - duodēvīcēsimus, -a, -um
19th - ūndēvīcēsimus, -a, -um
20th - vīcēsimus, -a, -um

100th - centēsimus, -a, -um   *1000th* - mīllēsimus, -a, -um

Declension of Ordinal Numerals

Latin ordinal numerals are declined just as any adjective of the first and second declension. (See page 30.)

Match the numerals to their names.

3rd	octō	XIV	duodēvīcēsimus	7th	decimus
XI	tertius	2nd	duodēvīgintī	10th	tredecim
VIII	duo	18th	secundus	IV	septimus
II	quīntus	XIX	ūndēvīgintī	1st	sextus
9th	ūndecim	XVIII	quattuordecim	6th	prīmus
5th	quīndecim	16th	sextus decimus	XIII	quattuor
20th	vīcēsimus	100th	septendecim	8th	septem
XV	nōnus	XVII	ūndecimus	VI	octāvus
M	mīlle	11th	centēsimus	VII	sex

☐ Flashcards - (Add the new cards.)

LET'S PRACTICE

Write the names of the Latin numerals. Include all three genders as needed.

1. XX

2. 12th

3. XII

4. 19th

5. II

6. IX

7. 4th

8. 17th

9. I

10. 14th

11. XVI

12. 15th

13. V

14. III

15. VIII

16. 13th

17. X

18. 1000th

☐ Flashcards

antīquus antīqua antīquum (adjective) means **ancient, old, former** antīquē (adverb) means **in former times**	**prō** (preposition - used with the ablative case) means **in front of, for, before, on behalf of, instead of**
errō errāre errāvī errātum means **wander, be mistaken, err**	**timeō** timēre timuī -* means **fear, be afraid**

Write the Latin words. (When more than one Latin word fits the definition, use the most recent word learned.)

in former times _____

winter _____

wish _____

ancient _____

fear _____

flee from _____

govern _____

wander _____

begin _____

not wish _____

in front of _____

citizen _____

*A dash indicates that no principal part exists for that form.

☐ Flashcards - (Add the new cards.)

LET'S PRACTICE

Match the words to their meanings.

tempus	because of
prō	I am afraid
propter	time
timeō	for
ergō	therefore
errō	I eat
edō	I am mistaken
antīquus	summer
animus	spirit
aestās	in former times
antīquē	old

Read the Latin sentences and translate.

1. Nautae semper in silvā errant, sed nōn amant avēs vidēre.

   It means _____

2. Līberī parvī timent novam patris eōrum nāvem ad īnsulam longam gubernāre.

   It means _____

3. Servīs filī eius numquam licet iacere pecūniam magistrī vestī in ignem.

   It means _____

4. Fābulās dē fortibus virīs antīquīs* parvae fīliae tuae saepe nārrō.

   It means _____

5. Patriam nostram amāmus, quā dē causā pugnāre prō eā dēbēmus.

   It means _____

*The adjective antīquus means *old* in the sense of ***old-fashioned*** or ***old-time*** rather than simply old in terms of age.

☐ Flashcards

Latin Workbook - Level 6
Copyright © 2006 by Karen Mohs

nihil (or nīl) (n.)* means nothing	oculus oculī (m.) means eye
mōs mōris (m.) means custom, habit mōrēs (mōrum) means **habits** or **character**	timor timōris (m.) means fear

Write the Latin words. (When more than one Latin word fits the definition, use the most recent word learned.)

not wish _____   custom _____

habits _____   nothing _____

fear _____   eye _____

be willing _____   on behalf of _____

begin _____

old _____

be afraid _____

steer _____

be mistaken _____

*A *defective noun* lacks some forms. The noun nihil lacks the genitive, dative, and ablative singular as well as all plural forms.

☐ Flashcards - (Add the new cards.)

LET'S PRACTICE

Match the words to their meanings.

mors	death
mōrēs	night
nox	character
mox	soon
nōlō	I am unwilling
nīl	nothing
neque	neither
tamen	it is proper
oculus	eye
timor	still
oportet	fear

Read the Latin sentences and translate.

1. Centum magistrī mīlle* puerōs puellāsque in lūdō magnō docent.

   It means _____

2. In viā cum filiō tuō multā nocte ambulās, sed nihil vidēre potes.

   It means _____

3. Grātiās dōnīs cibīsque agere est mōs antīquus atque amīcus.

   It means _____

4. Ad fenestram stātis et mortem senātūs vestrīs oculīs vidētis.

   It means _____

5. Hostēs ācrēs cōpiās nostrās monent, sed sine timōre inter arborēs errant.

   It means _____

*If singular, mīlle is an indeclinable *adjective*.

☐ Flashcards

84

lūx lūcis (f.) means **light** prīmā lūce means **at daybreak**	**spīrō** spīrāre spīrāvī spīrātum means **breathe, blow, exhale**
claudō claudere clausī clausum means **shut, close**	**iungō** iungere iūnxī iūnctum means **join**

Write the Latin words. (When more than one Latin word fits the definition, use the most recent word learned.)

nothing _____   eye _____

habit _____   light _____

at daybreak _____   character _____

err _____

join _____

shut _____

breathe _____

fear _____

former _____

☐ Flashcards - (Add the new cards.)

LET'S PRACTICE

Match the words to their meanings.

iungō	insult
iniūria	right
iūs	I help
iuvō	I join
cupiō	I desire
clāmō	I close
claudō	I shout
spēctō	I blow
lūx	at daybreak
spīrō	I look at
prīmā lūce	light

Read the Latin sentences and translate.

1. In agrīs et in oppidō spīrāre potest, sed sub aquā spīrāre nōn potest.

   It means _____

2. Prīmā lūce audēmus lapidēs super mūrum iacere et proelium statim incipere.

   It means _____

3. Amīcī sorōris meae tubam audiunt et oculōs eōrum claudunt. Perīcula bellī timent.

   It means _____

4. Prīmā nocte* rēx iubet virōs eius animālia interficere et cīvēs oppugnāre.

   It means _____

5. Poēta dīcit puellās in agrīs prīmā aestāte* cum frātribus eārum iungere.

   It means _____

*The adjective prīmus is used in prīmā aestāte (*at the beginning of summer*) and prīmā nocte (*early in the night*).

☐ Flashcards

Latin Workbook - Level 6
Copyright © 2006 by Karen Mohs

inimīcus	hūmānus
inimīcī (m.)	hūmāna hūmānum
	(adjective)
means	means
(personal) enemy	human, refined, cultivated
	hūmānē (adverb) means **politely, gently**
pervenīo	**inimīcus**
pervenīre pervēnī perventum*	inimīca inimīcum
	(adjective)
means	means
reach, arrive at	unfriendly, hostile
	inimīcē (adverb) means **with hostility**

Write the Latin words. (When more than one Latin word fits the definition, use the most recent word learned.)

light _____   politely _____

with
hostility _____   at daybreak _____

custom _____   (personal)
enemy _____

blow _____

reach _____

unfriendly _____

human _____

join _____

close _____

*The word **pervenīo** is a verb of motion and thus takes an *accusative of place to which* to complete its meaning.

☐ Flashcards - (Add the new cards.)

LET'S PRACTICE

Match the words to their meanings.

inveniō	I arrive at
interficiō	I kill
perveniō	I come upon
veniō	I come
inimīcē	poverty
inopia	hostile
inimīcus	with hostility
hūmānus	refined
īnsula	island
hūmānē	(personal) enemy
inimīcus	gently

Read the Latin sentences and translate.

1. Nāvem longam per fluctūs altōs gubernāmus et ad portum hodiē pervenīmus.

   It means _____

2. Multō diē inimīcus nōmen meum inimīcē appellat, sed fenestram fortiter claudō.

   It means _____

3. Medicus tamen nōs vēritātem dē gravī capite hūmānō docet.

   It means _____

4. Ergō prūdēns magister noster dīcit hominēs neque deōs neque animālia esse.

   It means _____

5. Cūr nautae miserī grātiam inimīcō nāvis dominō novē dēbent?

   It means _____

☐ Flashcards

pēs pedis (m.) means foot	**niger** nigra nigrum (adjective) means black
spērō spērāre spērāvī spērātum means hope	**albus** alba album (adjective) means white

Write the Latin words. (When more than one Latin word fits the definition, use the most recent word learned.)

foot _____

(personal) enemy _____

hostile _____

refined _____

black _____

hope _____

white _____

exhale _____

arrive at _____

light _____

fear _____

☐ Flashcards - (Add the new cards.)

LET'S PRACTICE

Match the words to their meanings.

superō	I surpass
spērō	I hope
spīrō	I blow
surgō	I stand up
pānis	foot
plēnus	full
pēs	bread
niger	deep
altus	black
albus	white
neque	neither

Read the Latin sentences and translate.

1. Centum avēs albae super agrōs nostrōs volant dum sub arbore sedēmus.

   It means _____

2. Nūntius animālia ācria timet, sed ducem eius videt et cupit spērāre.

   It means _____

3. Diēs est dum lūx clāra in caelō est, sed mediā nocte* lūx nōn clāra est.

   It means _____

4. Puella mē venīre iubet et dīcit prīmum equum nigrum trāns campum errāre.

   It means _____

5. Māter dīcit hominem duās manūs atque duōs pedēs atque ūnum capitem habēre.

   It means _____

*The phrase mediā nocte (literally translated ***middle of the night***) means ***at midnight***.

☐ Flashcards

90

LET'S PRACTICE

Translate these sentences into Latin.

1. Nothing frightens the son and daughter of the brave judge.
   _____
   _____

2. You (s.) seize the fierce black animal with two hands.
   _____
   _____

3. The citizen immediately begins to run with great fear.
   _____
   _____

4. We arrive at the new farmhouse and stay there.
   _____
   _____

5. She praises the fortune and character of the former queens.
   _____
   _____

6. I shut my eyes because he carries the horse's head.
   _____
   _____

7. He steers the ship into port and begins to hope.
   _____
   _____

8. He flees to his sister's farmhouse and joins her there.
   _____
   _____

9. Your (s.) beautiful daughter is always unfriendly to my father.
   _____
   _____

10. Winter is often a time to see white forests.
    _____
    _____

☐ Flashcards

TRANSLATION

Fill in the missing words from the list on the column. Macrons have been omitted.

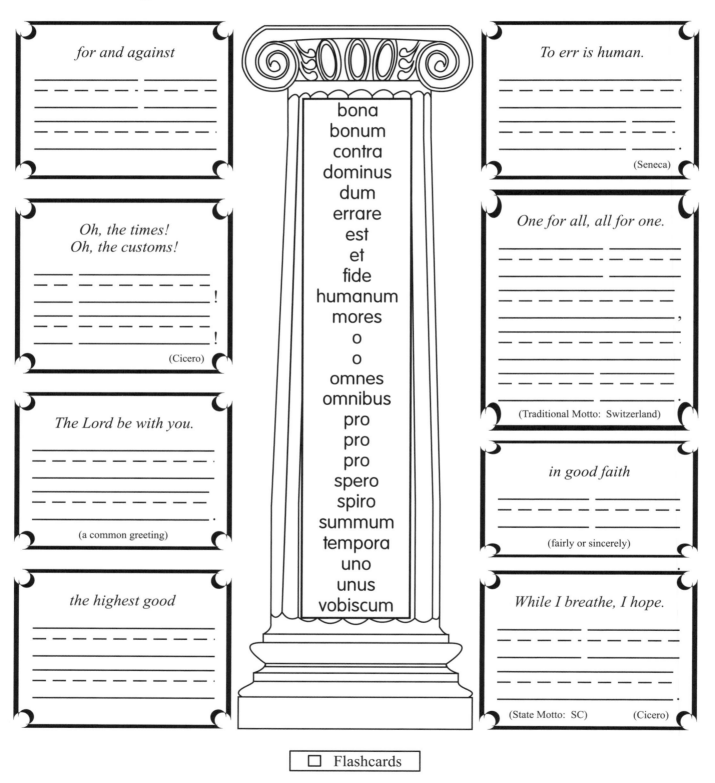

for and against

_____

_____

Oh, the times!
Oh, the customs!

_____ !

_____ !

(Cicero)

The Lord be with you.

_____

_____

(a common greeting)

the highest good

_____

_____

bona
bonum
contra
dominus
dum
errare
est
et
fide
humanum
mores
o
o
omnes
omnibus
pro
pro
pro
spero
spiro
summum
tempora
uno
unus
vobiscum

To err is human.

_____

_____ .

(Seneca)

One for all, all for one.

_____

_____ ,

_____

(Traditional Motto: Switzerland)

in good faith

_____

(fairly or sincerely)

While I breathe, I hope.

_____

(State Motto: SC)   (Cicero)

☐ Flashcards

Latin Workbook - Level 6
Copyright © 2006 by Karen Mohs

GENITIVE AND ABLATIVE CASE USES

Objective Genitive

(To indicate the *object* of a noun when that noun implies *feeling* or *action*, use a second noun in the genitive case. This *objective genitive* case, which connects two nouns, can be translated with words such as *for, of, from,* etc.)

timor mortis
the fear *of death*

magnam cūram hortōrum
great care *for the gardens*

spēs praemī
the hope *of reward*

dux cōpiārum
the leader *of the troops*

Partitive Genitive (Genitive of the Whole)

(To indicate the *whole* of which something is a part, use a noun in the genitive case. This noun in the genitive case follows the noun, pronoun, or adjective which designates the *part* of the whole.)

multitūdō hominum
a great number *of men*

multī nostrum
many *of us*

nihil cēnae
no dinner (nothing *of dinner*)

prīmus omnium
first *of all*

Careful! To indicate the *partitive* idea with certain words such as cardinal numbers, use dē or ex with the *ablative of place from which* instead of the *partitive genitive.*

Genitive of Description (Genitive of Measure) and Ablative of Description

(To describe the character, size, or quality of a noun which has a modifying adjective, use a second noun in either the genitive or the ablative case.)

Genitive of Description (Genitive of Measure)

liber magnae vēritātis
the book *of great truth*

socius parvōrum animōrum
the ally *of little courage*

The *genitive of description* is common in *definite measurement*, in which case it is called the *genitive of measure.*

arbor quīnque pedum
the five-foot tree (the tree *of five feet*)

Ablative of Description

liber magnā vēritāte
the book *of great truth*

socius parvīs animīs
the ally *of little courage*

The *ablative of description* is common in descriptions of *physical traits.*

animal ūnō cornū
the animal *with one horn*

Important note! In these two constructions, the genitive or ablative noun *must* have a modifying adjective.

☐ Flashcards - (Add the new cards.)

LET'S PRACTICE

Read the Latin sentences and translate. Circle the correct genitive or ablative case use.

1. Māter rēgīnae nostrae est potēns fēmina alta <u>pulchrīs oculīs nigrīs</u>.

   It means _____

   Objective Genitive   **Partitive Genitive**   **Genitive of Description**   **Ablative of Description**   **Genitive of Measure**

2. Vir miser <u>multum pecūniae</u> saepe cupit, sed cum dīligentiā numquam labōrat.

   It means _____

   Objective Genitive   **Partitive Genitive**   **Genitive of Description**   **Ablative of Description**   **Genitive of Measure**

3. In hortō nostrō <u>flōrēs quattuor pedum</u> nunc habēmus, sed eōs nōlō vidēre.

   It means _____

   Objective Genitive   **Partitive Genitive**   **Genitive of Description**   **Ablative of Description**   **Genitive of Measure**

4. Rēx laetus dīcit puerum nūntium fortem <u>summae audāciae</u> esse.*

   It means _____

   Objective Genitive   **Partitive Genitive**   **Genitive of Description**   **Ablative of Description**   **Genitive of Measure**

5. Cūr oportet <u>multōs liberōrum</u> lapidēs gravēs ad flūmen portāre?

   It means _____

   Objective Genitive   **Partitive Genitive**   **Genitive of Description**   **Ablative of Description**   **Genitive of Measure**

6. Fābulam antīquam dē <u>nostrā fugā gladiōrum et ignis</u> nōn amant.

   It means _____

   Objective Genitive   **Partitive Genitive**   **Genitive of Description**   **Ablative of Description**   **Genitive of Measure**

7. Amīcus servus tuus <u>magnā vōce</u> post iānuam albam celeriter sedet.

   It means _____

   Objective Genitive   **Partitive Genitive**   **Genitive of Description**   **Ablative of Description**   **Genitive of Measure**

*The Latin infinitive esse is the second principal part of the *being* verb. (See page 24.)

☐ Flashcards

Latin Workbook - Level 6
Copyright © 2006 by Karen Mohs

paucī paucae pauca (adjective) means few, a few	**rēs** reī (f.) means **thing, matter, affair** rēs novae means **revolution** rēs pūblica means **state**, **government**, or **republic**
pūblicus pūblica pūblicum (adjective) means public, belonging to the people pūblicē (adverb) means **publicly, officially**	**herba** herbae (f.) means grass

Write the Latin words. (When more than one Latin word fits the definition, use the most recent word learned.)

thing _____

grass _____

revolution _____

cultivated _____

public _____

white _____

black _____

hope _____

few _____

foot _____

publicly _____

state _____

☐ Flashcards - (Add the new cards.)

LET'S PRACTICE

Match the words to their meanings.

rēs	I dominate
rēs novae	revolution
rēgnō	matter
rēx	king
herī	grass
hiems	winter
herba	yesterday
paucī	officially
pūblicus	belonging to the people
rēs pūblica	government
pūblicē	a few

Read the Latin sentences and translate.

1. Lēgātus fortis contrā potentēs hostēs nostrōs rem* pūblicam nostram dēfendit.

    It means _____

2. Quā dē causā paucī ducēs audācēs paucōs** dē equīs fīliīs eōrum pūblicē dant?

    It means _____

3. Māter tua fidēlī eius sorōrī hūmānē dīcit eam rēs novās nōn amāre.

    It means _____

4. Octō līberī in herbā sedent et fābulās antīquās patriae eōrum audiunt.

    It means _____

*Because the Latin noun rēs has such broad use, an adequate English definition is difficult. Hence ***thing***, although given as one possibility, is rarely accurate in actual translation.

**As with cardinal numbers, paucī is followed by dē or ex and the *ablative of place from which* (see page 111) to express the *partitive* idea.

☐ Flashcards

falsus falsa falsum (adjective) means false, feigned, deceptive falsē (adverb) means **falsely**	**pars** partis (f.) means part, share, direction magna pars means **majority** or **greater part**
dubitō dubitāre dubitāvī dubitātum* means doubt, hesitate	**mōns** montis (m.) means mountain, hill

Write the Latin words. (When more than one Latin word fits the definition, use the most recent word learned.)

falsely _____   revolution _____

state _____   part _____

majority _____   mountain _____

grass _____   affair _____

doubt _____

public _____

a few _____

false _____

hope _____

*The verb dubitō, when meaning *I hesitate*, takes a *complementary infinitive*.

☐ Flashcards - (Add the new cards.)

LET'S PRACTICE

Match the words to their meanings.

mox	hill
mōns	death
mōs	soon
mors	habit
diū	for a long time
dubitō	as long as
dum	I hesitate
magna pars	share
falsus	falsely
pars	greater part
falsē	feigned

Read the Latin sentences and translate.

1. Pars nostrum in lūdō manet, sed pars vestrum ad nāvēs longās celeriter currit.

   It means _____

2. Septendecim nautae dubitant nāvem nigram ē portū prīmā lūce gubernāre.

   It means _____

3. Equus dēfessus nūntium rēgis ā montibus ad mare portat.

   It means _____

4. Malī agricolārum līberī fābulās falsās ad patrēs mātrēsque eōrum scrībunt.

   It means _____

5. Magna pars cīvium magnōs clāmōrēs et gladiōs ācrēs hostium timet.

   It means _____

□ Flashcards

Latin Workbook - Level 6
Copyright © 2006 by Karen Mohs

fēlīcitās fēlīcitātis (f.) means good luck, prosperity	**vulnus** vulneris (n.) means wound
lūna lūnae (f.) means moon	**reliquus** reliqua reliquum (adjective) means remaining, the rest of

Write the Latin words. (When more than one Latin word fits the definition, use the most recent word learned.)

hill _____   government _____

moon _____   wound _____

direction _____   greater part _____

remaining _____

deceptive _____

few _____

good luck _____

public _____

hesitate _____

☐ Flashcards - (Add the new cards.)

LET'S PRACTICE

Match the words to their meanings.

fēlīciter	I discover
reperiō	prosperity
reliquus	the rest of
fēlīcitās	successfully
lūx	play
lūdus	moon
lūna	light
volō	I want
vulnus	true
vērus	I wound
vulnerō	wound

Read the Latin sentences and translate.

1. Interim filius nautae fēlīcitātem atque grātiam rēgum antīquōrum videt.

   It means _____

2. Post aestātem magister reliquōs* līberōs ē silvā ad lūdum dūcit.

   It means _____

3. Fīlia vestra est trīstis quod secundam mēnsam cum eā edere numquam possum.

   It means _____

4. Sex vulnera eius videō et patrem meum in manibus meīs habeō ad multam noctem.

   It means _____

5. Fēmina oculōs claudit et dīcit poētam prūdentem multa dē terrā et lūnā scrībere.

   It means _____

*The adjective reliquus contains the idea *of* and is not used with a genitive. (See page 48.)

☐ Flashcards

100

sōl sōlis (m.) means sun	**excēdō** excēdere excessī excessum means leave, go out
corpus corporis (n.) means body	**officium** officī (n.) means duty

Write the Latin words. (When more than one Latin word fits the definition, use the most recent word learned.)

majority _____

sun _____

wound _____

mountain _____

leave _____

doubt _____

rest of _____

prosperity _____

feigned _____

duty _____

body _____

moon _____

share _____

☐ Flashcards - (Add the new cards.)

LET'S PRACTICE

Match the words to their meanings.

stō	duty
officium	I stand
sōl	sun
oportet	it is proper
exitus	way out
exspectō	I go out
excēdō	I await
carmen	wagon
corpus	head
caput	poem
carrus	body

Read the Latin sentences and translate.

1. Patrēs patriam eōrum dēfendunt, et filiī filiaeque in agrīs faciunt officium eōrum.

   It means _____

2. Amāmus noctem nam lūna est in caelō, sed amātis diem nam sōl est in caelō.

   It means _____

3. Dē verbīs servī sorōris tuae falsē dubitās quod dīcit eam tē amāre.

   It means _____

4. Agricolae falsī nōbīs grātiam dēbent oppidum post bellum excēdere.

   It means _____

5. Corpus hūmānum ūnum caput et duōs oculōs et duās manūs et duōs pedēs habet.

   It means _____

□ Flashcards

Latin Workbook - Level 6
Copyright © 2006 by Karen Mohs

impedīmentum
impedīmentī (n.)

means

hindrance, impediment

impedīmenta (impedīmentōrum) means **baggage**

putō
putāre putāvī putātum

means

think

pāx
pācis (f.)

means

peace

crēdō
crēdere crēdidī crēditum*

means

believe, trust

Write the Latin words. (When more than one Latin word fits the definition, use the most recent word learned.)

wound _____

duty _____

body _____

think _____

hindrance _____

believe _____

baggage _____

go out _____

remaining _____

moon _____

sun _____

peace _____

*The verb crēdō is used with the *dative* of the person believed or trusted or the *accusative* of the thing believed or trusted.

☐ Flashcards - (Add the new cards.)

LET'S PRACTICE

Match the words to their meanings.

paucī	I think
putō	peace
possum	few
pāx	I can
impedīmentum	hostile
inimīcus	baggage
impedīmenta	impediment
corpus	body
cōgō	I trust
crēdō	tomorrow
crās	I compel

Read the Latin sentences and translate.

1. Inimīcō tuō nōn crēdis, sed incipis verba vēra in librō antīquō crēdere.

    It means _____

2. Agricola dēfessus nōn putat tertiam puellam parvam in agrīs eius celeriter labōrāre.

    It means _____

3. Amīcō nostrō grātiam habēmus quod impedīmenta nostra per silvam portat.

    It means _____

4. Crēdō puerum fēlīcem ūndēvīgintī avēs nigrās albāsque in arboribus hodiē vidēre.

    It means _____

5. Post longum bellum omnēs dīcunt eōs pācem atque fēlīcitātem diū cupere.

    It means _____

☐ Flashcards

Latin Workbook - Level 6
Copyright © 2006 by Karen Mohs

LET'S PRACTICE

Translate these sentences into Latin.

1. To love her children is the duty of mothers.

2. They hesitate to carry the eight white stones out of the garden.

3. A few of the men defend the wall near the river.

4. The queen says that the king always fears peace.

5. A majority of the jurors live in small farmhouses.

6. The boys believe that their father carries a sword.

7. The leaders know that the lieutenant has a wound in the foot.

8. At daybreak my eyes do not see a bright sun.

9. He sits for a long time in the grass behind the mountain and listens to the birds.

10. I think that she is looking at us, but you (s.) think that she is eating.

☐ Flashcards

TRANSLATION

Fill in the missing words from the list on the column. Macrons have been omitted.

Nothing (is) new under the sun.

_____ _____ _____
_____ _____

the sum of the parts

_____ _____
_____

Prosperity has many friends.

_____ _____
_____ _____

amicos
diem
falsus
falsus
felicitas
habet
in
in
mortem
multos
nihil
novum
omnibus
partium
pax
per
post
pro
sole
sub
summa
tempore
uno
vobiscum

false in one thing, false in everything

_____ _____
_____ _____
_____ , _____
_____ _____

(a Roman legal principle)

for the time being

_____ _____

(a temporary situation)

Peace (be) with you.

_____ _____

(common farewell)

after death

_____ _____

(usually written postmortem)

by the day (each day)

_____ _____

(allowed expenses for one day)

□ Flashcards

Latin Workbook - Level 6
Copyright © 2006 by Karen Mohs

PRESENT PASSIVE INDICATIVE AND INFINITIVE
Conjugations

Two Voices of the Latin Verb

Active Voice: The subject of the sentence is ***doing an action***.

      Example: The man loves the woman.

Passive Voice: The subject is ***receiving an action***.

      Example: The man is being loved by the woman.

First Conjugation Present Passive Indicative

(The first conjugation *present passive infinitive* is amārī. It means *to be loved*.)

Singular

1st Person	amor means	**I am [being] loved.**
2nd Person	amāris means	**You (s.) are [being] loved.**
3rd Person	amātur means	**He (she, it) is [being] loved.**

Plural

1st Person	amāmur means	**We are [being] loved.**
2nd Person	amāminī means	**You (pl.) are [being] loved.**
3rd Person	amantur means	**They are [being] loved.**

Notice the two possible translations of the present passive indicative.
For example, the first person singular, amor, can mean either *I am loved* or *I am being loved*.

Second Conjugation Present Passive Indicative

(The second conjugation *present passive infinitive* is monērī. It means *to be warned*.)

Singular

1st Person	moneor means	**I am [being] warned.**
2nd Person	monēris means	**You (s.) are [being] warned.**
3rd Person	monētur means	**He (she, it) is [being] warned.**

Plural

1st Person	monēmur means	**We are [being] warned.**
2nd Person	monēminī means	**You (pl.) are [being] warned.**
3rd Person	monentur means	**They are [being] warned.**

Carefully compare the passive endings of all present passive indicative verbs.

☐ Flashcards - (Add the new cards.)

LET'S PRACTICE

Write the correct form of the Latin verbs voce and dēbeō.

1. She is called.

2. You (s.) are being called.

3. to be called

4. I am being owed.

5. We are owed.

6. He is owed.

7. They are being called.

8. She is being owed.

9. You (pl.) are called.

10. They are owed.

11. to be owed

12. We are being called.

13. You (s.) are owed.

14. You (pl.) are being owed.

15. He is being called.

☐ Flashcards

Latin Workbook - Level 6
Copyright © 2006 by Karen Mohs

PRESENT PASSIVE INDICATIVE AND INFINITIVE
Conjugations

Third Conjugation Present Passive Indicative
(The third conjugation *present passive **infinitive*** is dīcī. It means *to be told*.)

Singular

1st Person	dīcor means	**I am [being] told.**
2nd Person	dīceris means	**You** (s.) **are [being] told.**
3rd Person	dīcitur means	**He (she, it) is [being] told.**

Plural

1st Person	dīcimur means	**We are [being] told.**
2nd Person	dīciminī means	**You** (pl.) **are [being] told.**
3rd Person	dīcuntur means	**They are [being] told.**

Third Conjugation I-Stem Present Passive Indicative
(The third conjugation i-stem *present passive **infinitive*** is capī. It means *to be taken*.)

Singular

1st Person	capior means	**I am [being] taken.**
2nd Person	caperis means	**You** (s.) **are [being] taken.**
3rd Person	capitur means	**He (she, it) is [being] taken.**

Plural

1st Person	capimur means	**We are [being] taken.**
2nd Person	capiminī means	**You** (pl.) **are [being] taken.**
3rd Person	capiuntur means	**They are [being] taken.**

Fourth Conjugation Present Passive Indicative
(The fourth conjugation *present passive **infinitive*** is audīrī. It means *to be heard*.)

Singular

1st Person	audior means	**I am [being] heard.**
2nd Person	audīris means	**You** (s.) **are [being] heard.**
3rd Person	audītur means	**He (she, it) is [being] heard.**

Plural

1st Person	audīmur means	**We are [being] heard.**
2nd Person	audīminī means	**You** (pl.) **are [being] heard.**
3rd Person	audiuntur means	**They are [being] heard.**

☐ Flashcards - (Add the new cards.)

LET'S PRACTICE

Write the correct form of the Latin verbs claudō, accipiō, and reperiō.

1. He is being closed. _____

2. You (pl.) are discovered. _____

3. I am being received. _____

4. to be closed _____

5. They are received. _____

6. We are being closed. _____

7. She is being received. _____

8. You (s.) are being discovered. _____

9. to be discovered _____

10. We are received. _____

11. You (s.) are being closed. _____

12. I am discovered. _____

13. to be received _____

14. You (pl.) are being closed. _____

15. They are being discovered. _____

☐ Flashcards

110

ABLATIVE CASE USES

Ablative of Place From Which

(To indicate location *from which* motion takes place, use the prepositions ā/ab, dē, or ē/ex with the ablative case.)

	Singular	**Plural**
Use with ā/ab	Puella ab urbe currit.	Puella ab urbibus currit.
	The girl runs *away from the city*.	The girl runs *away from the cities*.
Use with dē	Dē viā venit.	Dē viīs venit.
	He comes *down from the road*.	He comes *down from the roads*.
Use with ē/ex	Mē ex agrō portat.	Mē ex agrīs portat.
	He carries me *out of the field*.	He carries me *out of the fields*.

Ablative of Personal Agent

(To indicate the *person* performing an action when the verb is *passive*,
use the preposition ā/ab with the ablative case.)

Singular	**Plural**
Ā puellā vocātur.	Ā puellīs vocātur.
He is called *by the girl*.	He is called *by the girls*.

Careful! The *ablative of means or instrument* is usually an **object** (and is used without a preposition),
whereas the *ablative of personal agent* is usually a **person** (and is used with the preposition ā/ab).

Ablative of Separation

(To indicate *separation* when there is *no* active movement,
use the ablative case with or without the preposition ā/ab.)

Use with ā/ab (usually with concrete nouns)	Dux mē ab urbe prohibet.
	The guide keeps me *away from the city*.
Use without ā/ab (usually with abstract nouns)	Dux mē cūrā līberat.
	The guide frees me *from anxiety*.

Ablative of Time When and Ablative of Time Within Which

(To indicate the *time when* an action occurs, use the ablative case without a preposition.)
(To indicate the *time within which* an action occurs, also use the ablative case without a preposition.)

Secundā hōrā venit.	Duōbus annīs venit.
He comes *at the second hour*.	He comes *within two years*.

☐ Flashcards - (Add the new cards.)

LET'S PRACTICE

Read the Latin sentences and translate. Write the correct ablative case use.*

1. Duodēvīgintī puerōs parvōs et eōrum sorōrēs <u>ā bellī perīculīs</u> dēfendimus.

   It means _____

   Ablative of _____

2. Similiter nauta miser novem epistulās mihi <u>in nāve</u> celeriter scrībit.

   It means _____

   Ablative of _____

3. Quīnque līberī agricolae amant <u>aestāte</u> currere et <u>hieme</u> dormīre.

   It means _____

   Ablative of _____

4. Pater māterque nūntiōs audiunt et medicum <u>verbīs eīs</u> laudant.

   It means _____

   Ablative of _____

5. Cūr fortēs virī nostrī <u>ab ācribus inimīcīs vestrīs</u> vulnerantur?

   It means _____

   Ablative of _____

6. Dēfessa soror tua īram fīlī eius videt et cōnsilium <u>tribus hōrīs</u> capit.

   It means _____

   Ablative of _____

7. Num fēminae puellaeque cupiunt <u>ab oppidō nostrō</u> currere?

   It means _____

   Ablative of _____

*See the appendix for a review of ablative case uses.

☐ Flashcards

Latin Workbook - Level 6
Copyright © 2006 by Karen Mohs

LET'S PRACTICE

Write the Latin verbs under the correct headings.

present active indicative	present passive indicative

agimur
audētis
cōgiminī
crēdis
cupimur
dormit
dubitāminī
errō
excēdunt
fugiō
gubernāris
iacitis
inciperis
invenior
iubētur
iungor
iuvantur
manent
perficiunt
pervenīs
pōnimus
prohibēminī
putātur
rapitur
redderis
rēgnās
sciuntur
sedet
spērāmus
spīrat
tenēmus
terreor
timentur
venīmus

☐ Flashcards

LET'S PRACTICE

Choose the best words for the sentences below and translate.

damur	dantur	dat	damini

1. Multa et pulchra dōna agricolae miserō et laetae eius fēminae _____ .

   It means _____

2. Prūdēns lēgāti filia duōs librōs eius filiō magistri saepe _____ .

   It means _____

3. Duodecim flōrēs albōs hodiē _____ quod hortum nōn habēmus.

   It means _____

4. Grātiam habētis et cum gaudiō clāmātis ubi praemium sacrum _____ .

   It means _____

terrēminī	relinqueris	portantur	dīcuntur

1. Fābulae dē rēgibus antīquīs ā patre meō quīntā hōrā semper _____ .

   It means _____

2. Magnīs vōcibus quīnque frātrum vestrōrum multā nocte _____ .

   It means _____

3. Cūr _____ ? Amīcī tuī nāvēs eōrum trāns mare gubernant.

   It means _____

4. Trēs sellae ad mēnsam _____ , sed līberī trīstēs edere nōn possunt.

   It means _____

☐ Flashcards

Latin Workbook - Level 6
Copyright © 2006 by Karen Mohs

LET'S PRACTICE

Circle the correct Latin verbs for the English meanings.

she is being helped	iuvātur iuvantur iuvor	you (s.) are conquered	vinciminī vinceris vincimur
you (pl.) are heard	audīris audīminī audīmur	they are being known	sciuntur scītur scior
they are doubted	dubitātur dubitāminī dubitantur	we are being judged	iūdicāminī iūdicāmur iūdicāris
I am being killed	interficior interficimur interficeris	they are ordered	iubentur iubētur iubēmur
we are being snatched	rapiminī rapimur rapitur	you (s.) are praised	laudātur laudāris laudor
it is being joined	iunguntur iungeris iungitur	you (pl.) are feared	timēminī timēmur timēris
you (s.) are moved	movēmur movēris movētur	we are being taught	docēmur docēris docentur

☐ Flashcards

PUZZLE TIME

Unscramble the following Latin words. Write them in the sentences below and translate.

aīlmnsu _____ .

aāimnu _____ .

āānrrrtu _____ .

eeīnrv _____ .

ceēfilm _____ .

adgīu _____ .

ginnrtuuu _____ .

aenrrt _____ .

1. Cūr fābula dē nāvibus longīs ā poētā amīcō hodiē _____ ?

   It means _____

2. Novem puellae parvae per _____ et trāns agrum agricolae _____ .

   It means _____

3. Putās equum _____ esse, quod herbam ad flūmen edere amat.

   It means _____

4. Pater māterque ab ūndecim līberīs eōrum sub monte statim _____ .

   It means _____

5. Simul atque nautae ad _____ perveniunt, incipiunt carmina avium audīre.

   It means _____

6. Fīlius septimus est plēnus _____ quod eī licet ad patriam _____ .

   It means _____

☐ Flashcards

ūsque (adverb) means all the way, all the time, even	**bibō** bibere bibī - means drink
stella stellae (f.) means star	**mēns** mentis (f.) means mind, thought

Write the Latin words. (When more than one Latin word fits the definition, use the most recent word learned.)

body _____   star _____

peace _____   all the way _____

mind _____   duty _____

baggage _____

trust _____

drink _____

impediment _____

think _____

leave _____

☐ Flashcards - (Add the new cards.)

LET'S PRACTICE

Match the words to their meanings.

brevī	soon
bibō	star
statim	I drink
stella	immediately
ūsque	where
ubi	city
urbs	all the time
mōns	thought
mōs	soon
mēns	habit
mox	mountain

Read the Latin sentences and translate.

1. Oportet mentēs līberōrum vestrōrum plēnās carminum antīquōrum dē iūre esse.

   It means _____

2. Parva soror nostra cupit numerōs ab ūnō ūsque ad centum hodiē scrībere.

   It means _____

3. Vōx rēgīnae tuae nōn audītur propter magnōs clāmōrēs inimīcōrum cīvium tuōrum.

   It means _____

4. Num nūntius amat cēnam eius edere et aquam eius bibere ad mēnsam?

   It means _____

5. Nocte lūcem sōlis nōn vidēs, sed potes lūnam stellāsque saepe vidēre.

   It means _____

☐ Flashcards

Latin Workbook - Level 6
Copyright © 2006 by Karen Mohs

certus	ventus
certus	**ventus**
certa certum	ventī (m.)
(adjective)	
means	means
sure, certain, reliable, diligent	wind
certē (adverb) means **certainly, surely**	

salūs	incertus
salūs	**incertus**
salūtis (f.)	incerta incertum
	(adjective)
means	means
safety, welfare, greeting	unsure, uncertain, doubtful
	incertē (adverb) means **uncertainly**

Write the Latin words. (When more than one Latin word fits the definition, use the most recent word learned.)

all the time _____   peace _____

star _____   thought _____

safety _____   wind _____

uncertainly _____   certainly _____

think _____

unsure _____

sure _____

drink _____

believe _____

☐ Flashcards - (Add the new cards.)

LET'S PRACTICE

Match the words to their meanings.

vērus	true
vulnus	wind
ventus	wound
vīta	life
servus	slave
sacer	welfare
salūs	holy
certus	uncertain
iniūria	body
incertus	certain
corpus	injury

Read the Latin sentences and translate.

1. Magnus ventus in silvā hodiē certē audītur, sed carmina avium nōn audiuntur.

   It means _____

2. Dux eōrum in equō eius audācter sedet, nam incertus est dē salūte rēgis eius.

   It means _____

3. Pater tuus cupit tē certum esse, sed in agrīs prīmā aestāte nōn labōrās.

   It means _____

4. Rēx dēfessus dē sellā eius incertē surgit et mortem filī eius nūntiat.

   It means _____

5. Fābula vestra dē pulchrī amīcī nostrī salūte nōs magnopere dēlectat.

   It means _____

□ Flashcards

probō	opus
probāre probāvī probātum	operis (n.)
means	means
prove, approve of, test	work, deed, workmanship

impediō	necesse
impedīre impedīvī impedītum	(defective adjective)*
means	means
hinder, impede, prevent	necessary, inevitable

Write the Latin words. (When more than one Latin word fits the definition, use the most recent word learned.)

work _____   uncertainly _____

mind _____   welfare _____

surely _____   necessary _____

even _____   wind _____

hinder _____

prove _____

drink _____

uncertain _____

certain _____

*The adjective **necesse** is defective. It has only nominative and accusative singular forms and is only used with the *being* verb.

☐ Flashcards - (Add the new cards.)

LET'S PRACTICE

Match the words to their meanings.

proelium   approve of

propter   battle

prō   on account of

probō   instead of

oportet   I attack

oppugnō   deed

opus   it is proper

impediō   I impede

impedīmenta   inevitable

necesse   baggage

neque   neither

Read the Latin sentences and translate.

1. Poētae vestrī in vīllīs opus eōrum faciunt, sed in nāvibus labōrāmus.

   It means _____

2. Puer cupit trēs flōrēs pulchrōs puellae dare, sed magnō timōre impeditur.

   It means _____

3. Edere et dormīre et spīrāre et labōrāre omnibus līberīs* necesse est.

   It means _____

4. Fīliī lēgātī sciunt prūdentem patrem eōrum librum septimum probāre.

   It means _____

5. Secunda mēnsa cum cūrā nōn parātur quod dominus ā servō nōn amātur.

   It means _____

*The adjective necesse is often used with the dative case.

☐ Flashcards

Latin Workbook - Level 6
Copyright © 2006 by Karen Mohs

labor	pugna
labōris (m.)	pugnae (f.)
means	means
difficulty, work, labor	fight
cernō	forum
cernere crēvī crētum	forī (n.)
means	means
distinguish, discern, understand	forum, marketplace

Write the Latin words. (When more than one Latin word fits the definition, use the most recent word learned.)

greeting _____

wind _____

forum _____

certainly _____

distinguish _____

doubtful _____

approve of _____

reliable _____

impede _____

inevitable _____

deed _____

difficulty _____

fight _____

☐ Flashcards - (Add the new cards.)

LET'S PRACTICE

Match the words to their meanings.

liber	book
lapis	stone
līber	free
labor	work
cernō	I trust
cēdō	I move
crēdō	I discern
porta	brave
pugna	marketplace
fortis	gate
forum	fight

Read the Latin sentences and translate.

1. Cūr caput equī ad agrum agricolae carrō nigrō multā nocte portātur?

   It means _____

2. Puellae gladiō vulnerantur, sed magistrō eōrum dē pugnā nōn dīcunt.

   It means _____

3. Paucae dē fēminīs ad forum hodiē ambulant et ōrātiōnēs virōrum eōrum audiunt.

   It means _____

4. Licet līberīs reliquīs sine magnō labōre cibum edere et aquam bibere.

   It means _____

5. Nāvem caelīs gubernās quod īnsulam oculīs tuīs cernere nōn potes.

   It means _____

□ Flashcards

vīvō	virtūs
vīvere vīxī vīctum	virtūtis (f.)
means	means
live, be alive	manliness, courage, virtue
prīncipium	**inquam**
prīncipī (n.)	(defective verb)*
means	means
beginning, origin	say

Write the Latin words. (When more than one Latin word fits the definition, use the most recent word learned.)

say _____   workmanship _____

fight _____   labor _____

manliness _____   marketplace _____

prevent _____

beginning _____

live _____

discern _____

test _____

*The verb **inquam** is defective. Its forms include **inquam** (*I say*), **inquis** (*you say*), **inquit** (*he, she, it says*), and **inquiunt** (*they say*). This word is used only with direct quotations. It is placed after the first word or phrase of the direct quotation.

☐ Flashcards - (Add the new cards.)

LET'S PRACTICE

Match the words to their meanings.

inquam	I command
iubeō	I say
incipiō	I hinder
impediō	I begin
proelium	battle
prīncipium	reward
praemium	origin
vīvō	wind
vērus	courage
virtūs	true
ventus	I am alive

Read the Latin sentences and translate.

1. Nūntius ducī fortī "Rēx noster" inquit "cupit gladium tuum hodiē portāre."

   It means _____

2. Nōnne virtūs iūdicis ā grātīs patriae eius cīvibus vidētur et laudātur?

   It means _____

3. Medicus vester prīncipium epistulae sorōrī eius dē mōribus malīs nautārum scrībit.

   It means _____

4. Avēs et hominēs in marī nōn vīvunt nam sub aquā spīrāre nōn possunt.

   It means _____

5. "Puellae" inquam "currere incipiunt quod sciunt puerōs lapidēs iacere."

   It means _____

☐ Flashcards

LET'S PRACTICE

Translate these sentences into Latin.

1. The fierce animal lives and breathes and frightens the two boys.

   _____

   _____

2. The safety of our troops is not certain, but uncertain.

   _____

   _____

3. "You (pl.) are wounded," she says, "but you (pl.) are not hindered."

   _____

   _____

4. The beginning of the story is told to the sons late at night.

   _____

   _____

5. The sailor is quickly joined by his twelve sons.

   _____

   _____

6. It certainly is necessary for the judge to hear the truth.

   _____

   _____

7. We often praise the virtue of your (pl.) leaders.

   _____

   _____

8. We teach the laws and customs of our land.

   _____

   _____

9. His teacher sees the fight and is not pleased.

   _____

   _____

10. "The women," they say, "are walking on the island."

    _____

    _____

☐ Flashcards

TRANSLATION

Fill in the missing words from the list on the column. Macrons have been omitted.

Principles prove,
they are not proved.

_____
_____
_____
_____

(Principles do not require proof.)

To sail is necessary,
to live is not necessary.

_____
_____
_____
_____
_____

(Gnaeus Pompeius)

from feet to head

_____
_____
_____
_____

a
ad
amicus
caput
cernitur
certus
de
est
est
est
fabula
filius
in
incerta
narratur
navigare
necesse
necesse
non
non
pars
patris
pedibus
principia
probant
probantur
re
te
usque
vivere

A son is part
of the father.

_____
_____
_____

(Legal maxim)

The story is
told about you.

_____
_____
_____
_____

(Horace)

A true friend is discerned
during an uncertain matter.

_____
_____
_____
_____

☐ Flashcards

IMPERFECT ACTIVE INDICATIVE
Conjugations

The Imperfect Tense

The *imperfect tense* is used for **continuous action** in past time. Because the Latin imperfect has no equivalent in English, use the helping verbs *was/were* or *used to.*

Examples: vocābam means **I was calling** or **I used to call.**

monēbant means **They were warning** or **they used to warn.**

(Depending on context, a Latin imperfect tense verb can also be translated with a simple English past tense verb, but this is very rare.)

First Conjugation Imperfect Active Indicative
(An imperfect tense indicator, -bā-, is placed between the present verb stem and the active ending.)

Singular

1st Person	amābam	means	**I was loving.**
2nd Person	amābās	means	**You (s.) were loving.**
3rd Person	amābat	means	**He (she, it) was loving.**

Plural

1st Person	amābāmus	means	**We were loving.**
2nd Person	amābātis	means	**You (pl.) were loving.**
3rd Person	amābant	means	**They were loving.**

Notice the macron on the vowel of the tense indicator. See the Rules for Macrons in the appendix.

Second Conjugation Imperfect Active Indicative
(An imperfect tense indicator, -bā-, is placed between the present verb stem and the active ending.)

Singular

1st Person	monēbam	means	**I was warning.**
2nd Person	monēbās	means	**You (s.) were warning.**
3rd Person	monēbat	means	**He (she, it) was warning.**

Plural

1st Person	monēbāmus	means	**We were warning.**
2nd Person	monēbātis	means	**You (pl.) were warning.**
3rd Person	monēbant	means	**They were warning.**

☐ Flashcards - (Add the new cards.)

LET'S PRACTICE

Write the correct form of the Latin verbs **vocō** and **dēbeō**.

1. I am owed.

2. We call.

3. You (pl.) were calling.

4. to be owed

5. They were owing.

6. You (pl.) are being called.

7. We were owing.

8. They were calling.

9. You (pl.) owe.

10. We are called.

11. I was owing.

12. You (s.) were owing.

13. to call

14. You (s.) were calling.

15. He was owing.

☐ Flashcards

IMPERFECT ACTIVE INDICATIVE
Conjugations

Third Conjugation Imperfect Active Indicative
(An imperfect tense indicator, -ēbā-, is placed between the present verb stem and the active ending.)

Singular

1st Person	dīcēbam means	**I was saying.**
2nd Person	dīcēbās means	**You (s.) were saying.**
3rd Person	dīcēbat means	**He (she, it) was saying.**

Plural

1st Person	dīcēbāmus means	**We were saying.**
2nd Person	dīcēbātis means	**You (pl.) were saying.**
3rd Person	dīcēbant means	**They were saying.**

Third Conjugation I-Stem Imperfect Active Indicative
(An imperfect tense indicator, -ēbā-, is placed between the present verb stem and the active ending.)

Singular

1st Person	capiēbam means	**I was taking.**
2nd Person	capiēbās means	**You (s.) were taking.**
3rd Person	capiēbat means	**He (she, it) was taking.**

Plural

1st Person	capiēbāmus means	**We were taking.**
2nd Person	capiēbātis means	**You (pl.) were taking.**
3rd Person	capiēbant means	**They were taking.**

Fourth Conjugation Imperfect Active Indicative
(An imperfect tense indicator, -ēbā-, is placed between the present verb stem and the active ending.)

Singular

1st Person	audiēbam means	**I was hearing.**
2nd Person	audiēbās means	**You (s.) were hearing.**
3rd Person	audiēbat means	**He (she, it) was hearing.**

Plural

1st Person	audiēbāmus means	**We were hearing.**
2nd Person	audiēbātis means	**You (pl.) were hearing.**
3rd Person	audiēbant means	**They were hearing.**

☐ Flashcards - (Add the new cards.)

IMPERFECT INDICATIVE
Conjugations

Imperfect Indicative of the "Being" Verb

Singular

1st Person	eram	means	**I was.**
2nd Person	erās	means	**You** (s.) **were.**
3rd Person	erat	means	**He** (**she, it**) **was.**

Plural

1st Person	erāmus	means	**We were.**
2nd Person	erātis	means	**You** (pl.) **were.**
3rd Person	erant	means	**They were.**

Notice the change in the imperfect tense vowel (ā) which is placed between the stem, er-, and the active ending.

Write the Latin verbs under the correct headings.

present active indicative	present passive indicative

imperfect active indicative	the "being" verb

audent
bibis
cernimus
eram
erāmus
erat
erātis
es
fugitis
impedior
incipitur
perveniēbātis
probābās
prohibēmur
putāminī
regēbat
spērābāmus
sunt
terrēbam
vīvēbant

☐ Flashcards - (Add the new card.)

IMPERFECT PASSIVE INDICATIVE
Conjugations

First Conjugation Imperfect Passive Indicative
(An imperfect tense indicator, -bā-, is placed between the present verb stem and the passive ending.)

Singular

1st Person	amābar means	I was being loved.
2nd Person	amābāris means	You (s.) were being loved.
3rd Person	amābātur means	He (she, it) was being loved.

Plural

1st Person	amābāmur means	We were being loved.
2nd Person	amābāminī means	You (pl.) were being loved.
3rd Person	amābantur means	They were being loved.

The imperfect passive can be translated with the helping verbs *used to be.*

Second Conjugation Imperfect Passive Indicative
(An imperfect tense indicator, -bā-, is placed between the present verb stem and the passive ending.)

Singular

1st Person	monēbar means	I was being warned.
2nd Person	monēbāris means	You (s.) were being warned.
3rd Person	monēbātur means	He (she, it) was being warned.

Plural

1st Person	monēbāmur means	We were being warned.
2nd Person	monēbāminī means	You (pl.) were being warned.
3rd Person	monēbantur means	They were being warned.

Circle the correct words.

we were being hindered	you (pl.) are being ordered	they used to be joined
impediēbāmus	iubēbāmus	iunguntur
impedīmus	iubēminī	iungitur
impedīmur	iubēbātis	iungunt
impediēbam	iubēbāminī	iungēbantur
impediēbāmur	iubētis	iungēbant

☐ Flashcards - (Add the new cards.)

LET'S PRACTICE

Write the correct form of the Latin verbs **vocō** and **dēbeō**.

1. They are called.

2. You (s.) were being owed.

3. He was calling.

4. They were being owed.

5. It is being owed.

6. I was being called.

7. You (s.) are called.

8. They owe.

9. We were being owed.

10. She calls.

11. I was being owed.

12. You (s.) were being called.

13. You (pl.) are owed.

14. She was being called.

15. It was being owed.

☐ Flashcards

Latin Workbook - Level 6
Copyright © 2006 by Karen Mohs

IMPERFECT PASSIVE INDICATIVE
Conjugations

Third Conjugation Imperfect Passive Indicative

(An imperfect tense indicator, -ēbā-, is placed between the present verb stem and the passive ending.)

Singular

1st Person	dīcēbar	means	**I was being told.**
2nd Person	dīcēbāris	means	**You (s.) were being told.**
3rd Person	dīcēbātur	means	**He (she, it) was being told.**

Plural

1st Person	dīcēbāmur	means	**We were being told.**
2nd Person	dīcēbāminī	means	**You (pl.) were being told.**
3rd Person	dīcēbantur	means	**They were being told.**

Third Conjugation I-Stem Imperfect Passive Indicative

(An imperfect tense indicator, -ēbā-, is placed between the present verb stem and the passive ending.)

Singular

1st Person	capiēbar	means	**I was being taken.**
2nd Person	capiēbāris	means	**You (s.) were being taken.**
3rd Person	capiēbātur	means	**He (she, it) was being taken.**

Plural

1st Person	capiēbāmur	means	**We were being taken.**
2nd Person	capiēbāminī	means	**You (pl.) were being taken.**
3rd Person	capiēbantur	means	**They were being taken.**

Fourth Conjugation Imperfect Passive Indicative

(An imperfect tense indicator, -ēbā-, is placed between the present verb stem and the passive ending.)

Singular

1st Person	audiēbar	means	**I was being heard.**
2nd Person	audiēbāris	means	**You (s.) were being heard.**
3rd Person	audiēbātur	means	**He (she, it) was being heard.**

Plural

1st Person	audiēbāmur	means	**We were being heard.**
2nd Person	audiēbāminī	means	**You (pl.) were being heard.**
3rd Person	audiēbantur	means	**They were being heard.**

☐ Flashcards - (Add the new cards.)

LET'S PRACTICE

Write the Latin verbs under the correct headings.

present active indicative

present passive indicative

imperfect active indicative

imperfect passive indicative

accipiēbāmus
audēbat
bibitis
cernēbar
clauduntur
cōgēbantur
convocābant
crēdunt
dubitābāris
errābam
excēdēbās
fugimus
gubernāminī
iaciēbāminī
impedīmur
incipior
iubēbant
iungēbāminī
iuvātis
mittēbāris
perficimur
pervenit
probāris
prohibeō
putābāmur
rēgnābātis
reperiēbātur
retinēbam
spērātur
spīrātis
timēbātur
vīvēbāmus

☐ Flashcards

vēndō vēndere vēndidī vēnditum means sell	**vereor** verērī veritus sum* means fear, respect
victōria victōriae (f.) means victory	**ōlim** (adverb) means once, formerly, at that time, some day

Write the Latin words. (When more than one Latin word fits the definition, use the most recent word learned.)

labor _____   fight _____

forum _____   courage _____

say _____   once _____

sell _____

be alive _____

fear _____

victory _____

origin _____

understand _____

*A *deponent* verb has passive forms, but active meanings. (See the footnote on page 61.)

☐ Flashcards - (Add the new cards.)

LET'S PRACTICE

Match the words to their meanings.

vēndō	I respect
vīvō	I sell
volō	I live
vereor	I want
ōrātiō	every
omnis	formerly
ōlim	speech
vēritās	I come
vincō	I conquer
victōria	victory
veniō	trueness

Read the Latin sentences and translate.

1. Num septendecim inimīcī tuī ventum et ignem in silvā verentur?

   It means _____

2. Ōlim fēminās et līberōs gladiō tuō fortiter dēfendēbās.

   It means _____

3. Magister eius fīliīs nostrīs "Decem equī" inquit "in forō hodiē vēndēbantur."

   It means _____

4. Nōnne dē perīculīs bellī ā patre prūdentī saepe monēbāris?

   It means _____

5. Post victōriam capiēbāminī cum cīvibus dēfessīs et in mare iaciēbāminī.

   It means _____

$\square$ Flashcards

cotīdiē (adverb) means daily, every day	**moror** morārī morātus sum* means delay
signum signī (n.) means sign, signal	**cōnscientia** cōnscientiae (f.) means awareness, knowledge, conscience

Write the Latin words. (When more than one Latin word fits the definition, use the most recent word learned.)

virtue _____ 　　say _____

formerly _____ 　marketplace _____

sign _____ 　　daily _____

victory _____

delay _____

awareness _____

respect _____

sell _____

live _____

*A *deponent* verb has passive forms, but active meanings. (See the footnote on page 61.)

☐ Flashcards - (Add the new cards.)

LET'S PRACTICE

Match the words to their meanings.

mors   death

moror   signal

signum   I delay

statim   at once

contrā   opposite

cotīdiē   every day

caelum   sky

cōnsilium   I establish

cōnscientia   I summon

cōnstituō   knowledge

cōnvocō   advice

Read the Latin sentences and translate.

1. Rēgīna mala docet puerum parvum ad flūmen diū morārī dēbēre.

   It means _____

2. Ad vīllam iūdicis ā lēgātō mittiminī, sed in oppidō nocte nōn dormītis.

   It means _____

3. Magnum signum ab omnibus agricolīs in terrā antīquā prīmā nocte audiēbātur.

   It means _____

4. Dum trēs frātrēs nostrī nāvēs gubernābant, epistulās eīs cotīdiē scrībēbāmus.

   It means _____

5. Vir "Cōnscientiam bonam" inquit "sine timōre poenae semper habeō."

   It means _____

☐ Flashcards

cōgitō cōgitāre cōgitāvī cōgitātum means think, plan, consider	**lavō** lavāre lāvī lautum means wash
lībertās lībertātis (f.) means freedom, liberty	**loquor** loquī locūtus sum* means speak, say, talk

Write the Latin words. (When more than one Latin word fits the definition, use the most recent word learned.)

every day _____   signal _____

fear _____

knowledge _____

wash _____

speak _____

sell _____

think _____

freedom _____

delay _____

*A *deponent* verb has passive forms, but active meanings. (See the footnote on page 61.)

☐ Flashcards - (Add the new cards.)

LET'S PRACTICE

Match the words to their meanings.

crēdō   I trust

cōgō   I plan

cernō   I understand

cōgitō   I compel

lībertās   children

liber   liberty

līberī   book

lavō   I wash

laudō   I praise

loquor   I am hard pressed

labōrō   I say

Read the Latin sentences and translate.

1. Quattuor puellae et quīnque puerī manūs eōrum in flūmine herī lavābant.

   It means _____

2. Dum pater in forō loquēbātur, māter aquam ad ignem portābat.

   It means _____

3. Cūr tredecim nautae dēfessī ā senātū potentī falsē laudantur?

   It means _____

4. Servus dē novā lībertāte eius incertus est, sed incipit mare mox amāre.

   It means _____

5. "Semper diū cōgitās" inquiunt magistrī, "sed numquam respondēs."

   It means _____

☐ Flashcards

māteria	**laus**
māteriae (f.)	laudis (f.)
means	means
material, subject matter, lumber	praise, fame
studium	**cōnor**
studī (n.)	cōnārī cōnātus sum*
means	means
eagerness, zeal, enthusiasm	try, attempt

Write the Latin words. (When more than one Latin word fits the definition, use the most recent word learned.)

sign _____

daily _____

eagerness _____

praise _____

liberty _____

plan _____

try _____

wash _____

material _____

say _____

conscience _____

*The *deponent* verb cōnor takes a *complementary infinitive*.

☐ Flashcards - (Add the new cards.)

LET'S PRACTICE

Match the words to their meanings.

cōnor   zeal

studium   I attempt

cōpia   plenty

statim   immediately

māteria   subject matter

magnopere   especially

maximē   greatly

lapis   glad

lātus   broad

laus   stone

laetus   fame

Read the Latin sentences and translate.

1. Cūr inimīcus tuus dīcit frātrem tuum librōs eius numquam memoriā tenēre.

   It means _____

2. Prīmā aestāte studium nautārum ā lēgātīs rēgis cotīdiē vidēbātur.

   It means _____

3. Septendecim agricolae dēfessī et filiī eōrum māteriam gravem ad vīllam portābant.

   It means _____

4. Līberōs vestrōs vēritātem docēre cōnāminī quod eōs vērē amātis.

   It means _____

5. Amīcus puerī "Laudāris" inquit, "sed crēdō laudem falsam esse."

   It means _____

□ Flashcards

144

tēlum tēlī (n.) means offensive weapons, missiles	**beneficium** beneficī (n.) means kindness, favor, benefit
pōns pontis (m.) means bridge	**trahō** trahere trāxī tractum means draw, drag, lead

Write the Latin words. (When more than one Latin word fits the definition, use the most recent word learned.)

fame _____ zeal _____

bridge _____ offensive weapon _____

consider _____

lumber _____

draw _____

freedom _____

kindness _____

attempt _____

talk _____

☐ Flashcards - (Add the new cards.)

LET'S PRACTICE

Match the words to their meanings.

trīstis	I surrender
trādō	I drag
trāns	over
trahō	grim
tempus	missile
tēlum	land
terra	time
beneficium	bridge
pōnō	well
bene	I locate
pōns	favor

Read the Latin sentences and translate.

1. Cōnābāmur nāvēs in portum herī vidēre, sed fluctūs vidēbāmus.

   It means _____

2. Cīvēs salūtī reī pūblicae cōnsilium capiēbant et tēla ad ducēs eōrum mittēbant.

   It means _____

3. Quōmodo omnēs puerī validī in ponte parvō multā nocte rapiēbantur?

   It means _____

4. Nūntius trīstis in silvā sedet quod dē beneficiīs rēgis nōn audit.

   It means _____

5. Carrus secundus post duōs equōs nigrōs puellae hodiē trahitur.

   It means _____

☐ Flashcards

LET'S PRACTICE

Translate these sentences into Latin.

1. Your friends were being seized by your enemies in the marketplace.

2. Five carts are being dragged through the small town.

3. The poet was listening to the birds and was finishing the song.

4. It is necessary to begin work at daybreak.

5. The fierce animals were certainly being feared by the citizens.

6. It is proper to think first and to answer wisely.

7. Mother says, "A good boy washes his hands."

8. While the brother was sleeping, his sister was walking.

9. In summer I am unwilling to do my duty every day.

10. Therefore the letter is received with great joy.

☐ Flashcards

TRANSLATION

Fill in the missing words from the list on the column. Macrons have been omitted.

The workmanship was better than the subject matter.

_____

_____

_____

(Ovid)

To accept a favor is to sell freedom.

_____

_____

_____

(Publilius Syrus)

Hand washes hand.

_____

_____

(A favor for a favor.)   (Petronius)

accipere
beneficium
cogito
conscientiam
ergo
est
famam
laudis
lavat
libertatem
manum
manus
materiam
multi
omnes
opus
pauci
studio
sum
superabat
trahimur
vendere
verentur

I think, therefore I am.

_____ ,

_____ .

(Descartes)

We are all led on by our eagerness for praise.

_____

_____

_____

(Cicero)

Many fear their reputation, few their conscience.

_____ ,

_____

(Pliny)

☐ Flashcards

148

FUTURE ACTIVE INDICATIVE AND INFINITIVE
Conjugations

The Future Tense

In Latin, as in English, the ***future tense*** is used to describe an action that will take place in the future. The Latin future tense is translated into English using the helping words *shall* and *will*.

First Conjugation Future Active Indicative

(A future tense indicator, -bi-, is placed between the present verb stem and the active ending.)
(The first conjugation *future active **infinitive**** is amātūrus [-a, -um] esse. It means *to be about to love*.)

Singular

1st Person	amābō means	**I shall love.**
2nd Person	amābis means	**You (s.) will love.**
3rd Person	amābit means	**He (she, it) will love.**

Plural

1st Person	amābimus means	**We shall love.**
2nd Person	amābitis means	**You (pl.) will love.**
3rd Person	amābunt means	**They will love.**

The vowel (i) of the future tense indicator (bi) changes to ō in the first person singular and to u in the third person plural.

Second Conjugation Future Active Indicative

(A future tense indicator, -bi-, is placed between the present verb stem and the active ending.)
(The second conjugation *future active **infinitive*** is monitūrus [-a, -um] esse. It means *to be about to warn*.)

Singular

1st Person	monēbō means	**I shall warn.**
2nd Person	monēbis means	**You (s.) will warn.**
3rd Person	monēbit means	**He (she, it) will warn.**

Plural

1st Person	monēbimus means	**We shall warn.**
2nd Person	monēbitis means	**You (pl.) will warn.**
3rd Person	monēbunt means	**They will warn.**

Again, notice the change in the vowel of the future tense indicator.

*To form the future active infinitive, add -ūrus, -ūra, -ūrum to the stem of the fourth principal part, followed by esse.

☐ Flashcards - (Add the new cards.)

LET'S PRACTICE

Write the correct form of the Latin verbs voco and dēbeō.

1. You (pl.) were being owed.

2. We shall call.

3. You (pl.) will owe.

4. to be about to call

5. You (pl.) were owing.

6. She will call.

7. You (s.) will owe.

8. She is being called.

9. You (s.) are being owed.

10. I shall call.

11. You (pl.) were being called.

12. They will call.

13. He will owe.

14. We were being called.

15. to be about to owe

☐ Flashcards

150

FUTURE ACTIVE INDICATIVE AND INFINITIVE
Conjugations

Third Conjugation Future Active Indicative
(A future tense indicator, -ē-, is placed between the present verb stem and the active ending.)
(The third conjugation *future active* **infinitive** is dīctūrus [-a, -um] esse. It means *to be about to say*.)

Singular

1st Person	dīcam means	**I shall say.**
2nd Person	dīcēs means	**You (s.) will say.**
3rd Person	dīcet means	**He (she, it) will say.**

Plural

1st Person	dīcēmus means	**We shall say.**
2nd Person	dīcētis means	**You (pl.) will say.**
3rd Person	dīcent means	**They will say.**

Again, notice the change in the future tense indicator.

Third Conjugation I-Stem Future Active Indicative
(A future tense indicator, -ē-, is placed between the present verb stem and the active ending.)
(The third conjugation i-stem *future active* **infinitive** is captūrus [-a, -um] esse. It means *to be about to take*.)

Singular

1st Person	capiam means	**I shall take.**
2nd Person	capiēs means	**You (s.) will take.**
3rd Person	capiet means	**He (she, it) will take.**

Plural

1st Person	capiēmus means	**We shall take.**
2nd Person	capiētis means	**You (pl.) will take.**
3rd Person	capient means	**They will take.**

Again, notice the change in the future tense indicator.

Circle the correct tense for each Latin verb.

trahēmus	present	imperfect	future
cōgitābātis	present	imperfect	future
incipiet	present	imperfect	future
rapiunt	present	imperfect	future

☐ Flashcards - (Add the new cards.)

FUTURE ACTIVE INDICATIVE AND INFINITIVE
Conjugations

Fourth Conjugation Future Active Indicative
(A future tense indicator, -ē-, is placed between the present verb stem and the active ending.)
(The fourth conjugation *future active **infinitive*** is audītūrus [-a, -um] esse. It means *to be about to hear*.)

Singular

1st Person	audiam means	**I shall hear.**
2nd Person	audiēs means	**You** (s.) **will hear.**
3rd Person	audiet means	**He (she, it) will hear.**

Plural

1st Person	audiēmus means	**We shall hear.**
2nd Person	audiētis means	**You** (pl.) **will hear.**
3rd Person	audient means	**They will hear.**

Again, notice the change in the future tense indicator.

Future Indicative of the "Being" Verb
(The *future **infinitive*** of the "being" verb is futūrus [-a, -um] esse. It means *to be about to be*.)

Singular

1st Person	erō means	**I shall be.**
2nd Person	eris means	**You** (s.) **will be.**
3rd Person	erit means	**He (she, it) will be.**

Plural

1st Person	erimus means	**We shall be.**
2nd Person	eritis means	**You** (pl.) **will be.**
3rd Person	erunt means	**They will be.**

Notice the change in the future tense vowel (i) which is placed between the stem, er-, and the active ending.

Circle the correct tense for each Latin verb.

fugiēbant	present	imperfect	future
eritis	present	imperfect	future
impedīs	present	imperfect	future
dormiēbat	present	imperfect	future
iubēbunt	present	imperfect	future

☐ Flashcards - (Add the new cards.)

FUTURE PASSIVE INDICATIVE
Conjugations

First Conjugation Future Passive Indicative
(A future tense indicator, -bi-, is placed between the present verb stem and the passive ending.)*

Singular

1st Person	amābor	means	**I shall be loved.**
2nd Person	amāberis	means	**You (s.) will be loved.**
3rd Person	amābitur	means	**He (she, it) will be loved.**

Plural

1st Person	amābimur	means	**We shall be loved.**
2nd Person	amābiminī	means	**You (pl.) will be loved.**
3rd Person	amābuntur	means	**They will be loved.**

Pay careful attention to the change in the vowel of the future tense indicator.

Second Conjugation Future Passive Indicative
(A future tense indicator, -bi-, is placed between the present verb stem and the passive ending.)

Singular

1st Person	monēbor	means	**I shall be warned.**
2nd Person	monēberis	means	**You (s.) will be warned.**
3rd Person	monēbitur	means	**He (she, it) will be warned.**

Plural

1st Person	monēbimur	means	**We shall be warned.**
2nd Person	monēbiminī	means	**You (pl.) will be warned.**
3rd Person	monēbuntur	means	**They will be warned.**

Again, pay careful attention to the change in the vowel of the future tense indicator.

Match the words to their meanings.

probābantur	You (s.) will prove
probābis	I am being proved
probābiminī	We shall be proved
probor	They were being proved
probābimur	You (pl.) will be proved

*Future passive infinitives are rare and are therefore not included in this workbook.

☐ Flashcards - (Add the new cards.)

LET'S PRACTICE

Write the correct form of the Latin verbs voco and dēbeō.

1. We shall be owed.

2. She will be called.

3. You (s.) will call.

4. I shall be owed.

5. They will be called.

6. They were being called.

7. It will be owed.

8. We were calling.

9. They will owe.

10. You (s.) will be called.

11. I shall owe.

12. We shall be called.

13. You (pl.) will call.

14. We shall owe.

15. You (pl.) will be owed.

☐ Flashcards

FUTURE PASSIVE INDICATIVE
Conjugations

Third Conjugation Future Passive Indicative
(A future tense indicator, -ē-, is placed between the present verb stem and the passive ending.)*

Singular

1st Person	dīcar	means	**I shall be told.**
2nd Person	dīcēris	means	**You (s.) will be told.**
3rd Person	dīcētur	means	**He (she, it) will be told.**

Plural

1st Person	dīcēmur	means	**We shall be told.**
2nd Person	dīcēminī	means	**You (pl.) will be told.**
3rd Person	dīcentur	means	**They will be told.**

Third Conjugation I-Stem Future Passive Indicative
(A future tense indicator, -ē-, is placed between the present verb stem and the passive ending.)*

Singular

1st Person	capiar	means	**I shall be taken.**
2nd Person	capiēris	means	**You (s.) will be taken.**
3rd Person	capiētur	means	**He (she, it) will be taken.**

Plural

1st Person	capiēmur	means	**We shall be taken.**
2nd Person	capiēminī	means	**You (pl.) will be taken.**
3rd Person	capientur	means	**They will be taken.**

Fourth Conjugation Future Passive Indicative
(A future tense indicator, -ē-, is placed between the present verb stem and the passive ending.)*

Singular

1st Person	audiar	means	**I shall be heard.**
2nd Person	audiēris	means	**You (s.) will be heard.**
3rd Person	audiētur	means	**He (she, it) will be heard.**

Plural

1st Person	audiēmur	means	**We shall be heard.**
2nd Person	audiēminī	means	**You (pl.) will be heard.**
3rd Person	audientur	means	**They will be heard.**

*Note the change in the future tense indicator in the first person singular and the third person plural forms.

☐ Flashcards - (Add the new cards.)

LET'S PRACTICE

Translate these Latin verbs.

inveniō _____   invenīmus _____

invenīs _____   invenītis _____

invenit _____   inveniunt _____

spērābo _____   spērābimus _____

spērābis _____   spērābitis _____

spērābit _____   spērābunt _____

dubitor _____   dubitāmur _____

dubitāris _____   dubitāminī _____

dubitātur _____   dubitantur _____

moror _____   morāmur _____

morāris _____   morāminī _____

morātur _____   morantur _____

terrēbar _____   terrēbāmur _____

terrēbāris _____   terrēbāminī _____

terrēbātur _____   terrēbantur _____

iaciar _____   iaciēmur _____

iaciēris _____   iaciēminī _____

iaciētur _____   iacientur _____

dūcēbam _____   dūcēbāmus _____

dūcēbās _____   dūcēbātis _____

dūcēbat _____   dūcēbant _____

☐ Flashcards

LET'S PRACTICE

Circle the correct Latin translations of the English words in the first column.

you (pl.) will be pleased	dēlectābiminī	dēlectābāminī	dēlectāminī
he will send	mittit	mittet	mittor
you (s.) will try	cōnāberis	cōnābāris	cōnāris
I am being held back	retinēbam	retinēbar	retineor
they were daring	audēbunt	audēbant	audent
you (s.) were leaving	excēdēs	excēdis	excēdēbās
we were running	currēmus	currēbāmus	currimus
it will be told	nārrābitur	nārrābātur	nārrātur
you (pl.) were being led	dūciminī	dūcēbāminī	dūcēminī
I shall say	loquar	loquor	loquēbar
he was sitting	sedēbit	sedēbās	sedēbat
they will sleep	dormiet	dormiunt	dormient
it is being steered	gubernātur	gubernantur	gubernābātur
you (pl.) will prove	probābātis	probātis	probābitis
I shall be helped	iuvābor	iuvor	iuvābar
I was being seized	rapiar	rapiēbar	rapiēbāris
they will be judged	iūdicābantur	iūdicābuntur	iūdicantur
we shall wander	errābāmus	errāmus	errābimus
it will be found	reperītur	reperientur	reperiētur
you (s.) say	inquis	inquitis	inquiunt
we shall be ordered	iubēbiminī	iubēbimur	iubēberis

☐ Flashcards

LET'S PRACTICE

Write the Latin verbs under the correct headings.

present active indicative
_____
_____
_____
_____
_____
_____

present passive indicative
_____
_____
_____
_____
_____
_____

imperfect active indicative
_____
_____
_____
_____
_____
_____

imperfect passive indicative
_____
_____
_____
_____
_____
_____

future active indicative
_____
_____
_____
_____
_____
_____

future passive indicative
_____
_____
_____
_____
_____
_____

ambulātur
appellat
cernentur
clāmāmur
claudēbās
cōgitābāminī
dēligēbam
docēmus
fugiēs
gerēbātur
habēminī
habitābātis
impediar
incipis
interficient
iunget
laudantur
lavābiminī
movēbāris
pervenītis
prohibēbat
putābant
relinquō
scrībēbāmur
timēberis
trahimur
vēndēbar
vidēbimur
vīvam
vulnerābitis

☐ Flashcards

LET'S PRACTICE

Circle the correct tense for each Latin verb.

accipiuntur	present	imperfect	future
scīmur	present	imperfect	future
nāvigābātur	present	imperfect	future
cupiētur	present	imperfect	future
bibō	present	imperfect	future
dīcitur	present	imperfect	future
spīrābās	present	imperfect	future
rēgnābunt	present	imperfect	future
audiēris	present	imperfect	future
monēbar	present	imperfect	future
temptābimur	present	imperfect	future
respondēris	present	imperfect	future
amor	present	imperfect	future
manēbant	present	imperfect	future
capiēbāris	present	imperfect	future
āmittēminī	present	imperfect	future
pugnābimus	present	imperfect	future
perficiēbāmur	present	imperfect	future
verēminī	present	imperfect	future
cōgar	present	imperfect	future
dēbēbuntur	present	imperfect	future

☐ Flashcards

LET'S PRACTICE

Translate these Latin verbs.

prohibēbor	_____	prohibēbimur	_____
prohibēberis	_____	prohibēbiminī	_____
prohibēbitur	_____	prohibēbuntur	_____
impedior	_____	impedīmur	_____
impedīris	_____	impedīminī	_____
impedītur	_____	impediuntur	_____
cernō	_____	cernimus	_____
cernis	_____	cernitis	_____
cernit	_____	cernunt	_____
putābam	_____	putābāmus	_____
putābās	_____	putābātis	_____
putābat	_____	putābant	_____
fugiam	_____	fugiēmus	_____
fugiēs	_____	fugiētis	_____
fugiet	_____	fugient	_____
cōnor	_____	cōnāmur	_____
cōnāris	_____	cōnāminī	_____
cōnātur	_____	cōnantur	_____
iungēbar	_____	iungēbāmur	_____
iungēbāris	_____	iungēbāminī	_____
iungēbātur	_____	iungēbantur	_____

☐ Flashcards

FINAL REVIEW

Translate the following Latin words.

spērō	_____	amīcus	_____
iuvō	_____	excēdō	_____
errō	_____	prō	_____
albus	_____	stella	_____
vēndō	_____	lavō	_____
moror	_____	incertus	_____
cōgō	_____	studium	_____
bibō	_____	pugna	_____
sōl	_____	cōnscientia	_____
aestās	_____	lībertās	_____
timor	_____	reliquus	_____
virtūs	_____	vōx	_____
caput	_____	grātiam habeō	_____
propter	_____	beneficium	_____
loquor	_____	tempus	_____
pāx	_____	iungō	_____
novus	_____	ōlim	_____
flūmen	_____	fugiō	_____
pars	_____	tēlum	_____
herba	_____	prīmā lūce	_____
cīvis	_____	opus	_____
vulnus	_____	nīl	_____
mēns	_____	cotīdiē	_____
falsus	_____	perveniō	_____
inimīcus *(n.)*	_____	trahō	_____
necesse	_____	lūna	_____
putō	_____	laus	_____
oportet	_____	rēs pūblica	_____
crēdō	_____	fēlīcitās	_____
certus	_____	nāvis	_____
dubitō	_____	prohibeō	_____
iubeō	_____	ignis	_____

☐ Flashcards

FINAL REVIEW

Fill in the chart with the correct adjective endings.

	Masculine Singular	Feminine Singular	Neuter Singular	Masculine Plural	Feminine Plural	Neuter Plural
Dat.	simil____	simil____	simil____	simil____	simil____	simil____
Gen.	audāc____	audāc____	audāc____	audāc____	audāc____	audāc____
Acc.	nov____	nov____	nov____	nov____	nov____	nov____
Nom.	ācer____	ācr____	ācr____	ācr____	ācr____	ācr____
Gen.	cert____	cert____	cert____	cert____	cert____	cert____
Abl.	nigr____	nigr____	nigr____	nigr____	nigr____	nigr____
Acc.	fēlīc____	fēlīc____	fēlix____	fēlīc____	fēlīc____	fēlīc____
Gen.	brev____	brev____	brev____	brev____	brev____	brev____
Dat.	fals____	fals____	fals____	fals____	fals____	fals____
Acc.	grāt____	grāt____	grāt____	grāt____	grāt____	grāt____
Nom.	alb____	alb____	alb____	alb____	alb____	alb____
Acc.	trīst____	trīst____	trīst____	trīst____	trīst____	trīst____

☐ Flashcards

FINAL REVIEW

Translate the following Latin words.

carmen	_____	mox	_____
dēbeō	_____	iniūria	_____
prīmā nocte	_____	rēs	_____
salūs	_____	ūsque	_____
grātia	_____	hiems	_____
grātus	_____	parātus	_____
probō	_____	volō	_____
līber	_____	cōgitō	_____
magna pars	_____	signum	_____
vērus	_____	nihil	_____
dum	_____	incipiō	_____
iūs	_____	plēnus	_____
oculus	_____	pūblicus	_____
pēs	_____	vereor	_____
impedīmentum	_____	claudō	_____
forum	_____	cōnor	_____
ventus	_____	mōs	_____
inimīcus (adj.)	_____	rēgnō	_____
mediā nocte	_____	labor	_____
rēs novae	_____	pōns	_____
vīvō	_____	antīquus	_____
cernō	_____	mōns	_____
licet	_____	timeō	_____
possum	_____	niger	_____
hūmānus	_____	nōlō	_____
officium	_____	victōria	_____
summus	_____	inquam	_____
prīncipium	_____	paucī	_____
impediō	_____	bellum	_____
lūx	_____	corpus	_____
audeō	_____	māteria	_____
gubernō	_____	spīrō	_____

☐ Flashcards

FINAL REVIEW

For the noun stems below, circle the correct genders and declensions. Write the endings.

<table>
<tr>
<td>

Gender: masculine feminine neuter
Declension: 1st 2nd 3rd 3rd-I 4th 5th

vulnus _____   vulner _____
vulner _____   vulner _____
vulner _____   vulner _____
vulnus _____   vulner _____
vulner _____   vulner _____

</td>
<td>

Gender: masculine feminine neuter
Declension: 1st 2nd 3rd 3rd-I 4th 5th

r _____   r _____
r _____   r _____
r _____   r _____
r _____   r _____
r _____   r _____

</td>
</tr>
<tr>
<td>

Gender: masculine feminine neuter
Declension: 1st 2nd 3rd 3rd-I 4th 5th

nāv _____   nāv _____
nāv _____   nāv _____
nāv _____   nāv _____
nāv _____   nāv _____
nāv _____   nāv _____

</td>
<td>

Gender: masculine feminine neuter
Declension: 1st 2nd 3rd 3rd-I 4th 5th

pugn _____   pugn _____
pugn _____   pugn _____
pugn _____   pugn _____
pugn _____   pugn _____
pugn _____   pugn _____

</td>
</tr>
<tr>
<td>

Gender: masculine feminine neuter
Declension: 1st 2nd 3rd 3rd-I 4th 5th

ocul _____   ocul _____
ocul _____   ocul _____
ocul _____   ocul _____
ocul _____   ocul _____
ocul _____   ocul _____

</td>
<td>

Gender: masculine feminine neuter
Declension: 1st 2nd 3rd 3rd-I 4th 5th

animal _____   animāl _____
animāl _____   animāl _____
animāl _____   animāl _____
animal _____   animāl _____
animāl _____   animāl _____

</td>
</tr>
</table>

☐ Flashcards

FINAL REVIEW

For the noun stems below, circle the correct genders and declensions. Write the endings.

Gender: masculine feminine neuter
Declension: 1st 2nd 3rd 3rd-I 4th 5th

timor _____   timōr _____

timōr _____   timōr _____

timōr _____   timōr _____

timōr _____   timōr _____

timōr _____   timōr _____

Gender: masculine feminine neuter
Declension: 1st 2nd 3rd 3rd-I 4th 5th

portus _____   port _____

port _____   port _____

port _____   port _____

port _____   port _____

port _____   port _____

Gender: masculine feminine neuter
Declension: 1st 2nd 3rd 3rd-I 4th 5th

laus _____   laud _____

laud _____   laud _____

laud _____   laud _____

laud _____   laud _____

laud _____   laud _____

Gender: masculine feminine neuter
Declension: 1st 2nd 3rd 3rd-I 4th 5th

pōns _____   pont _____

pont _____   pont _____

pont _____   pont _____

pont _____   pont _____

pont _____   pont _____

Gender: masculine feminine neuter
Declension: 1st 2nd 3rd 3rd-I 4th 5th

corn _____   corn _____

corn _____   corn _____

corn _____   corn _____

corn _____   corn _____

corn _____   corn _____

Gender: masculine feminine neuter
Declension: 1st 2nd 3rd 3rd-I 4th 5th

sign _____   sign _____

sign _____   sign _____

sign _____   sign _____

sign _____   sign _____

sign _____   sign _____

☐ Flashcards

FINAL REVIEW

For the verb stems below, circle the conjugation and write the principal parts and endings.

Conjugation: *1st 2nd 3rd 3rd-I 4th 5th*

Principal parts: _____

present active	imperfect active	future active
iung____ iung____	iung____ iung____	iung____ iung____
iung____ iung____	iung____ iung____	iung____ iung____
iung____ iung____	iung____ iung____	iung____ iung____

present passive	imperfect passive	future passive
iung____ iung____	iung____ iung____	iung____ iung____
iung____ iung____	iung____ iung____	iung____ iung____
iung____ iung____	iung____ iung____	iung____ iung____

Conjugation: *1st 2nd 3rd 3rd-I 4th 5th*

Principal parts: _____

present active	imperfect active	future active
put____ put____	put____ put____	put____ put____
put____ put____	put____ put____	put____ put____
put____ put____	put____ put____	put____ put____

present passive	imperfect passive	future passive
put____ put____	put____ put____	put____ put____
put____ put____	put____ put____	put____ put____
put____ put____	put____ put____	put____ put____

☐ Flashcards

FINAL REVIEW

For the verb stems below, circle the conjugation and write the principal parts and endings.

Conjugation: 1st 2nd 3rd 3rd-I 4th 5th

Principal parts: _____

present active		*imperfect active*		*future active*	
iub ____	iub ____	iub ____	iub ____	iub ____	iub ____
iub ____	iub ____	iub ____	iub ____	iub ____	iub ____
iub ____	iub ____	iub ____	iub ____	iub ____	iub ____

present passive		*imperfect passive*		*future passive*	
iub ____	iub ____	iub ____	iub ____	iub ____	iub ____
iub ____	iub ____	iub ____	iub ____	iub ____	iub ____
iub ____	iub ____	iub ____	iub ____	iub ____	iub ____

Conjugation: 1st 2nd 3rd 3rd-I 4th 5th

Principal parts: _____

present active		*imperfect active*		*future active*	
imped ____	imped ____	imped ____	imped ____	imped ____	imped ____
imped ____	imped ____	imped ____	imped ____	imped ____	imped ____
imped ____	imped ____	imped ____	imped ____	imped ____	imped ____

present passive		*imperfect passive*		*future passive*	
imped ____	imped ____	imped ____	imped ____	imped ____	imped ____
imped ____	imped ____	imped ____	imped ____	imped ____	imped ____
imped ____	imped ____	imped ____	imped ____	imped ____	imped ____

☐ Flashcards

FINAL REVIEW

For the verb stem below, circle the conjugation and write the principal parts and endings.

Conjugation: *1st 2nd 3rd 3rd-I 4th 5th*

Principal parts: _____

present active	*imperfect active*	*future active*

iac ____ iac _____   iac _____ iac _____   iac _____ iac _____

iac ____ iac _____   iac _____ iac _____   iac _____ iac _____

iac ____ iac _____   iac _____ iac _____   iac _____ iac _____

present passive	*imperfect passive*	*future passive*

iac ____ iac _____   iac _____ iac _____   iac _____ iac _____

iac ____ iac _____   iac _____ iac _____   iac _____ iac _____

iac ____ iac _____   iac _____ iac _____   iac _____ iac _____

Write the principal parts and forms of the "being" verb. On the line beneath each form, write the meaning.

Principal parts: _____

present	*imperfect*	*future*

☐ Flashcards

FINAL REVIEW

Match the Latin present tense active and passive verbs to their infinitive forms.

_____ 1. cōgō   a. claudī

_____ 2. dēbeor   b. dēbēre

_____ 3. claudor   c. cōgere

_____ 4. impediō   d. impedīrī

_____ 5. cōgor   e. impedīre

_____ 6. dēbeō   f. dēbērī

_____ 7. impedior   g. cōgī

_____ 8. dubitor   h. incipere

_____ 9. incipiō   i. prohibērī

_____ 10. prohibeō   j. prohibēre

_____ 11. gubernor   k. dubitāre

_____ 12. prohibeor   l. dubitārī

_____ 13. dubitō   m. incipī

_____ 14. incipior   n. gubernārī

Read the Latin sentences and translate.

1. Pater eōrum, "Duo equī," inquit, "reliqua impedīmenta in forum portābunt."

   It means _____

2. Dum pānem edēbam, fīlius meus et amīcī eius ad pontem ambulābant.

   It means _____

3. Quīnque carrī novī ā lēgātīs nostrīs per viās urbis tuae mox trahentur.

   It means _____

4. In nāve sex hōrās manēbimus, nam nauta stellās vidēre nōn potest.

   It means _____

5. Crāsne cum tribus frātribus tuīs in silvā diū eris?

   It means _____

6. Agricola parātus dē igne in agrō ad vīllam eius monēbitur.

   It means _____

7. Animālia clāmōribus terrēbantur et in summō monte currēbant.

   It means _____

☐ Flashcards

PUZZLE TIME

Write the Latin meanings of the English words on the puzzle below.

across

1. I hold back
3. across
4. I respect
8. I wash
13. head
14. I approve of
16. inevitable
17. enthusiasm
18. I consider
20. memory
22. duty
25. I grant
26. sun
28. I think
29. poem
32. down from
33. eye
34. your
38. ___ nocte (at midnight)
39. ancient
40. I hope
41. swift
43. part
44. I arrive at
46. sign
48. grass
50. hill
52. I leave
55. it is
57. nothing
58. unfriendly
59. freedom
60. safety
61. territory

down

1. ready
2. kindness
3. foot
4. voice
5. I rule
6. because of
7. I dare
8. praise
9. once
10. I exhale
11. even
12. I stand
15. I drink
17. at once
18. awareness
19. willingly
21. thought
23. justice
24. lumber
27. true
30. friendly
31. thousand
35. toward
36. peace
37. I shut
39. summer
40. star
42. king
45. I come
47. soon
49. well
50. custom
51. I am unwilling
52. I wander
53. tomorrow
54. onto
55. out of
56. there

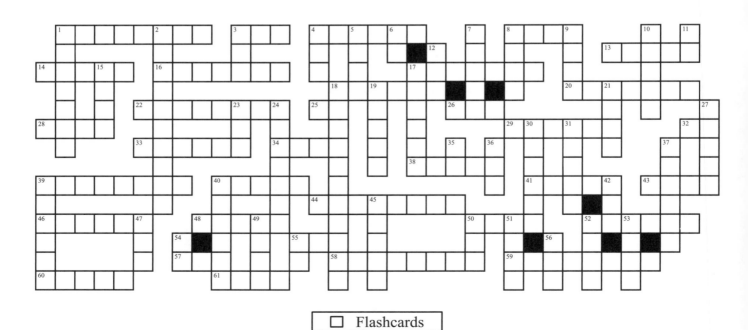

Flashcards

APPENDIX

Latin - English Glossary

a

ā, ab - *prep. (with abl.)*, from, away from, by (7, 13); **ā dextrā** - on the right (13); **ā dextrō cornū** - on the right wing (13); **ā sinistrō cornū** - on the left wing (13); **ā tergō** - in the rear (13)

ā dextrā - on the right (13)

ā dextrō cornū - on the right wing (13)

ā sinistrō cornū - on the left wing (13)

ā tergō - in the rear (13)

ab - See **ā, ab**.

accipiō, accipere, accēpī, acceptum - receive, accept (3)

ācer, ācris, ācre - *adj.*, sharp, fierce (9)

ācriter - *adv.*, sharply, fiercely

ad - *prep. (with acc.)*, to, near, toward, for, at (7); **ad multam noctem** - until late at night (13)

ad multam noctem - until late at night (13)

adhūc - *adv.*, up to this time, still (13)

adventus, adventūs (m.) - arrival, approach (9)

aestās, aestātis (f.) - summer (65); **prīmā aestāte** - at the beginning of summer (86)

ager, agrī (m.) - field, territory (3)

agō, agere, ēgī, āctum - drive, do (3); **grātiās agō** - give thanks (13)

agricola, agricolae (m.) - farmer (3)

albus, alba, album - *adj.*, white (89)

altē - *adv.*, on high, deeply

altus, alta, altum - *adj.*, high, tall, deep (9)

ambulō, ambulāre, ambulāvī, ambulātum - stroll, walk (3)

amīcē - *adv.*, in a friendly way (61)

amīcitia, amīcitiae (f.) - friendship, friendliness (3)

amīcus, amīca, amīcum - *adj.*, friendly (61)

amīcus, amīcī (m.) - friend (3)

āmittō, āmittere, āmīsī, āmissum - lose (3)

amō, amāre, amāvī, amātum - love, like (3)

animal, animālis (n.) - animal (9)

animus, animī (m.) - mind, spirit; (pl., courage) (9)

annus, annī (m.) - year (3)

ante - *prep. (with acc.)*, before, in front of (13)

antīquē - *adv.*, in former times (81)

antīquus, antīqua, antīquum - *adj.*, ancient, old, former (81)

appellō, appellāre, appellāvī, appellātum - address, call, name (3)

aqua, aquae (f.) - water (3)

arbor, arboris (f.) - tree (9)

arma, armōrum (pl. n.) - arms, weapons, defensive arms, weapons for close fighting (9)

atque - *conj.*, and, and also, and even, as (7); **simul atque** - as soon as (13)

audācia, audāciae (f.) - boldness, daring (3)

audācter - *adv.*, boldly, rashly (11)

audāx (*genitive:* **audācis**) - *adj.*, bold, daring (11)

audeō, audēre, ausus sum - *semi-dep.*, dare (61)

audiō, audīre, audīvī, audītum - hear, listen to (3)

aut - *conj.*, or (13)

aut ... aut - either ... or (13)

avis, avis (f.) - bird (9)

b

bellum, bellī (n.) - war (53); **bellum gerō** - wage war (13)

bene - *adv.*, well, fully (7)

beneficium, beneficī (n.) - kindness, favor, benefit (145)

bibō, bibere, bibī, (-) - drink (117)

bonus, bona, bonum - *adj.*, good (9)

brevī - in a short time, soon

brevī tempore - in a short time, soon (13)

brevis, breve - *adj.*, short, brief (13); **brevī** - in a short time, soon; **brevī tempore** - in a short time, soon (13)

breviter - *adv.*, briefly

c

caelum, caelī (n.) - sky, heavens (5)

campus, campī (m.) - field, plain (3)

capiō, capere, cēpī, captum - take, capture (5); **cōnsilium capiō** - form (make) a plan (5)

captīvus, captīvī (m.) - captive, prisoner (5)

caput, capitis (n.) - head (59)

Note: The number in parentheses indicates the page on which the vocabulary word is introduced.

APPENDIX

Latin - English Glossary

carmen, carminis (n.) - song,
    poem (45)

carrus, carrī (m.) - cart, wagon (5)

castra ... moveō - break camp (13)

causa, causae (f.) - cause, reason
    (3); quā dē causā - for which
    reason (13)

cēdō, cēdere, cessī, cessum
    - move, give way, yield,
    withdraw (5)

celer, celeris, celere - *adj.*, quick,
    swift, speedy (9)

celeriter - *adv.*, quickly, swiftly

cēna, cēnae (f.) - dinner (9)

centēsimus, -a, -um - *ordinal*
    num., one hundredth (79)

centum - *cardinal num.*, one
    hundred (C) (77)

cernō, cernere, crēvī, crētum
    - distinguish, discern,
    understand (123)

certē - *adv.*, certainly, surely (119)

certus, certa, certum - *adj.*, sure,
    certain, reliable, diligent (119)

cibus, cibī (m.) - food (9)

cīvis, cīvis (m. or f.) - citizen (67)

clāmō, clāmāre, clāmāvī,
    clāmātum - shout (5)

clāmor, clāmōris (m.) - shout,
    noise (9)

clārē - *adv.*, clearly, brightly,
    famously

clārus, clāra, clārum - *adj.*, clear,
    bright, famous (5)

claudō, claudere, clausī, clausum
    - shut, close (85)

cōgitō, cōgitāre, cōgitāvī,
    cōgitātum - think, plan,
    consider (141)

cōgō, cōgere, coēgī, coāctum
    - *(may take objective infinitive)*,
    collect, compel (51)

cōnfirmō, cōnfirmāre, cōnfirmāvī,
    cōnfirmātum - strengthen,
    encourage, declare (5)

cōnor, cōnārī, cōnātus sum - *dep.*
    (takes complementary
    infinitive), try, attempt (143)

cōnscientia, cōnscientiae (f.)
    - awareness, knowledge,
    conscience (139)

cōnsilium, cōnsilī (n.) - plan,
    advice, foresight (5);
    cōnsilium capiō - form (make)
    a plan (5)

cōnstituō, cōnstituere, cōnstituī,
    cōnstitūtum - set up,
    determine, decide, establish
    (5); diem cōnstituō - appoint
    a day (13)

contrā - *prep. (with acc.)*, against,
    opposite (13)

convocō, convocāre, convocāvī,
    convocātum - call together,
    assemble, summon (5)

cōpia, cōpiae (f.) - plenty, supply;
    (pl., troops, forces) (3)

cornū, cornūs (n.) - horn, wing (of
    an army) (5); ā dextrō cornū
    - on the right wing (13); ā
    sinistrō cornū - on the left
    wing (13)

corpus, corporis (n.) - body (101)

cotīdiē - *adv.*, daily, every day (139)

crās - *adv.*, tomorrow (7)

crēdō, crēdere, crēdidī, crēditum
    - *(takes dat. of person, acc. of*
    thing), believe, trust (103)

cum - *prep. (with abl.)*, along with,
    with (7)

cupiō, cupere, cupīvī, cupītum
    - wish, want, desire (5)

cūr - *interrogative adv.*, why? (7)

cūra, cūrae (f.) - care, anxiety (5)

currō, currere, cucurrī, cursum
    - run (9)

d

dē - *prep. (with abl.)*, down from,
    from, about, concerning, of
    (7); quā dē causā - for which
    reason (13)

dēbeō, dēbēre, dēbuī, dēbitum
    - *(takes infinitive)*, owe, aught
    (53); grātiam dēbeō - *(takes*
    dat. of person), am under an
    obligation (53)

decem - *cardinal num.*, ten (X)
    (77)

decimus, -a, -um - *ordinal num.*,
    tenth (79)

dēfendō, dēfendere, dēfendī,
    dēfēnsum - defend (3)

dēfessus, dēfessa, dēfessum
    - *adj.*, tired (13)

dēlectō, dēlectāre, dēlectāvī,
    dēlectātum - please (3)

dēligō, dēligere, dēlēgī, dēlēctum
    - choose (3)

dēmōnstrō, dēmōnstrāre,
    dēmōnstrāvī, dēmōnstrātum
    - point out, show (3)

deus, deī (m.) - god (7)

dexter, dextra, dextrum - *adj.*,
    right, right-hand (9); ā dextrā
    - on the right (13); ā dextrō
    cornū - on the right wing (13)

APPENDIX

Latin - English Glossary

dexterē - *adv.*, skillfully

dīcō, dīcere, dīxī, dictum - say, tell (3)

diem cōnstituō - appoint a day (13)

diēs, diēī (m. & f.) - day (7); diem cōnstituō - appoint a day (13); multō diē - late in the day (13)

dīligentia, dīligentiae (f.) - diligence, care (7)

diū - *adv.*, for a long time, long (7)

dō, dare, dedī, datum - give, grant (3)

doceō, docēre, docuī, doctum - (*with two acc.*), teach, show, inform (9)

dominus, dominī (m.) - master, lord, owner (7)

dōnum, dōnī (n.) - gift, present (7)

dormiō, dormīre, dormīvī, dormītum - sleep (9)

dubitō, dubitāre, dubitāvī, dubitātum - (*takes complementary infinitive when meaning hesitate*), doubt, hesitate (97)

dūcō, dūcere, dūxī, ductum - lead, bring (3)

dum - *conj.*, while, until, as long as (47)

duo, duae, duo - *cardinal num.*, two (II) (77)

duodecim - *cardinal num.*, twelve (XII) (77)

duodecimus, -a, -um - *ordinal num.*, twelfth (79)

duodēvīcēsimus, -a, -um - *ordinal num.*, eighteenth (79)

duodēvīgintī - *cardinal num.*, eighteen (XVIII) (77)

dux, ducis (m.) - leader, guide (7)

e

ē, ex - *prep. (with abl.)*, out of, from, of (13)

ea - *demonstrative pro. (nom.)*, she; *(nom.)*, they (n.); *(acc.)*, them (n.) (73)

eā - *demonstrative pro. (abl.)*, with/by/from her (73)

eae - *demonstrative pro. (nom.)*, they (f.) (73)

eam - *demonstrative pro. (acc.)*, her (73)

eārum - *demonstrative pro. (gen.)*, of them (their) (f.) (73)

eās - *demonstrative pro. (acc.)*, them (f.) (73)

ecce - *interj.*, behold (7)

edō, edere, ēdī, ēsum - eat (5)

ego - *personal pro. (nom.)*, I (71)

eī - *demonstrative pro. (dat.)*, to/for him/her/it; *(nom.)*, they (m.) (73)

eīs - *demonstrative pro. (dat.)*, to/for them (m. or f. or n.); *(abl.)*, with/by/from them (m. or f. or n.) (73)

eius - *demonstrative pro. (gen.)*, of him/her/it (his/her/its) (73)

eō - *demonstrative pro. (abl.)*, with/by/from him/it (73)

eōrum - *demonstrative pro. (gen.)*, of them (their) (m. or n.) (73)

eōs - *demonstrative pro. (acc.)*, them (m. or n.) (73)

epistula, epistulae (f.) - letter, epistle (7)

equus, equī (m.) - horse (7)

ergō - *adv.*, therefore, then (7)

errō, errāre, errāvī, errātum - wander, be mistaken, err (81)

es - *2nd person sing. of* sum (24)

esse - *(infinitive of the "being" verb)*, to be (24)

est - *3rd person sing. of* sum (24); - he is, she is, it is, there is (7)

estis - *2nd person pl. of* sum (24)

et - *conj.*, and, also, even (7)

et ... et - *conj.*, both ... and (13)

etiam - *adv.*, also, even (7); nōn sōlum ... sed etiam - not only ... but also (13)

eum - *demonstrative pro. (acc.)*, him (73)

ex - See ē, ex.

excēdō, excēdere, excessī, excessum - leave, go out (101)

exitus, exitūs (m.) - departure, way out, outcome, end (7)

exspectō, exspectāre, exspectāvī, exspectātum - await, wait for (5)

f

fābula, fābulae (f.) - story (3)

facilis, facile - *adj.*, easy (11)

faciō, facere, fēcī, factum - make, do (9); iter faciō - march (9)

falsē - *adv.*, falsely (97)

falsus, falsa, falsum - *adj.*, false, feigned, deceptive (97)

fāma, fāmae (f.) - report, rumor, reputation (3)

APPENDIX

Latin - English Glossary

fēlīcitās, fēlīcitātis (f.) - good luck, prosperity (99)

fēlīciter - *adv.*, happily, successfully, fortunately (11)

fēlix (*genitive:* **fēlīcis**) - *adj.*, happy, fortunate, lucky (11)

fēmina, fēminae (f.) - woman, wife (3)

fenestra, fenestrae (f.) - window (11)

fidēlis, fidēle - *adj.*, faithful, loyal (11)

fidēliter - *adv.*, faithfully, loyally

fidēs, fideī (f.) - faith, loyalty, pledge, confidence (11)

filia, filiae (f.) - daughter (3)

filius, filī (m.) - son (3)

flōs, flōris (m.) - flower (11)

fluctus, fluctūs (m.) - wave (11)

flūmen, flūminis (n.) - flowing, river, stream (47)

fortis, forte - *adj.*, brave (11)

fortiter - *adv.*, bravely

fortūna, fortūnae (f.) - fortune, chance, luck (3)

forum, forī (n.) - forum, marketplace (123)

frāter, frātris (m.) - brother (11)

frūmentum, frūmentī (n.) - grain (11)

fuga, fugae (f.) - flight, exile (3)

fugiō, fugere, fūgī, fugitum - flee, flee from, avoid (65)

g

gaudium, gaudī (n.) - joy, gladness (7)

gēns, gentis (f.) - nation, family, clan (7)

gerō, gerere, gessī, gestum - bear, carry on, wear (13); **bellum gerō** - wage war (13)

gladius, gladī (m.) - sword (7)

grātē - *adv.*, gratefully, pleasantly, willingly (49)

grātia, grātiae (f.) - gratitude, influence, favor (59); **grātiam dēbeō** - *(takes dat. of person)*, am under an obligation (53); **grātiam habeō** - *(takes dat. of person)*, feel gratitude (59); **grātiās agō** - give thanks (13)

grātiās agō - give thanks (13)

grātus, grāta, grātum - *adj.*, pleasing, welcome, thankful (49)

gravis, grave - *adj.*, heavy, severe, serious (13)

graviter - *adv.*, weightily, heavily, seriously, grievously, deeply, severely

gubernō, gubernāre, gubernāvī, gubernātum - steer, navigate, govern (65)

h

habeō, habēre, habuī, habitum - have, hold, keep, consider, regard (5); **grātiam habeō** - *(takes dat. of person)*, feel gratitude (59); **ōrātiōnem habeō** - deliver a speech (13)

habitō, habitāre, habitāvī, habitātum - live, dwell (5)

herba, herbae (f.) - grass (95)

herī - *adv.*, yesterday (7)

hiems, hiemis (f.) - winter (65)

hodiē - *adv.*, today (7)

homō, hominis (m. or f.) - human being, man (9)

hōra, hōrae (f.) - hour (7)

hortus, hortī (m.) - garden (9)

hostis, hostis (m.) - enemy (of the State) (9); (pl., the enemy) (9)

hūmānē - *adv.*, politely, gently (87)

hūmānus, hūmāna, hūmānum - *adj.*, human, refined, cultivated (87)

i

iaciō, iacere, iēcī, iactum - throw (5)

iam - *adv.*, now, already (7)

iānua, iānuae (f.) - door (9)

ibi - *adv.*, there, in that place (9)

id - *demonstrative pro. (nom. or acc.)*, it (73)

ignis, ignis (m.) - fire (59)

iī - *demonstrative pro. (nom.)*, they (m. or n.) (73)

impedīmentum, impedīmentī (n.) - hindrance, impediment (103); **impedīmenta, impedīmentōrum** - baggage (103)

impediō, impedīre, impedīvī, impedītum - hinder, impede, prevent (121)

in - *prep. (with acc.)*, into, onto, against, toward, for; *prep. (with abl.)*, in, on, upon, over (7)

incertē - *adv.*, uncertainly (119)

incertus, incerta, incertum - *adj.*, unsure, uncertain, doubtful (119)

incipiō, incipere, incēpī, inceptum - begin (67)

APPENDIX

Latin - English Glossary

inimīcē - *adv.*, with hostility (87)

inimīcus, inimīca, inimīcum - *adj.*, unfriendly, hostile (87)

inimīcus, inimīcī (m.) - (personal) enemy (87)

iniūria, iniūriae (f.) - injustice, insult, injury (49)

inopia, inopiae (f.) - want, lack, need, poverty (9)

inquam - *defective verb (only sing. and third person pl. forms; only with direct quotations; placed after first word or phrase)*, say (125)

inquis - *(second person sing. of inquam)*, you (s.) say (125)

inquit - *(third person sing. of inquam)*, he, she, it says (125)

inquiunt - *(third person pl. of inquam)*, they say (125)

īnsula, īnsulae (f.) - island (3)

inter - *prep. (with acc.)*, between, among (9)

interficiō, interficere, interfēcī, interfectum - kill (5)

interim - *adv.*, meanwhile (7)

inveniō, invenīre, invēnī, inventum - come upon, find (5)

īra, īrae (f.) - anger, wrath (9)

is - *demonstrative pro. (nom.)*, he (73)

itaque - *adv.*, and so, therefore (11)

iter, itineris (n.) - route, journey, march (9); iter faciō - march (9)

iter faciō - march (9)

iubeō, iubēre, iussī, iussum - *(takes objective infinitive)*, order, command, bid (51)

iūdex, iūdicis (m.) - juror, judge (9)

iūdicō, iūdicāre, iūdicāvī, iūdicātum - judge, consider (5)

iungō, iungere, iūnxī, iūnctum - join (85)

iūs, iūris (n.) - right, law, justice (63)

iuvō, iuvāre, iūvī, iūtum - help, do good to (49)

I

labor, labōris (m.) - difficulty, work, labor (123)

labōrō, labōrāre, labōrāvī, labōrātum - labor, suffer, am hard pressed (5)

laetē - *adv.*, happily, joyfully, gladly

laetus, laeta, laetum - *adj.*, happy, joyful, glad (13)

lapis, lapidis (m.) - stone (9)

lātē - *adv.*, widely

lātus, lāta, lātum - *adj.*, wide, broad (13)

laudō, laudāre, laudāvī, laudātum - praise (5)

laus, laudis (f.) - praise, fame (143)

lavō, lavāre, lāvī, lautum - wash (141)

lectus, lectī (m.) - dining couch, bed (9)

lēgātus, lēgātī (m.) - lieutenant, ambassador, envoy (3)

lēx, lēgis (f.) - law (3)

liber, librī (m.) - book (9)

liber, libera, liberum - *adj.*, free (45); liberī, liberōrum - (masc. pl.) children (45)

liberō, liberāre, liberāvī, liberātum - set free, free (5)

lībertās, lībertātis (f.) - freedom, liberty (141)

licet - *impersonal verb (takes dat. and often infinitive)*, it is permitted (63)

lingua, linguae (f.) - tongue, language (3)

littera, litterae (f.) - letter (of the alphabet) (3); (pl., epistle, letter) (13)

locus, locī (m.) - place, location, situation (3)

longē - *adv.*, far, by far, far off

longus, longa, longum - *adj.*, long (referring to space) (13); nāvis longa - battleship (13)

loquor, loquī, locūtus sum - *dep.*, speak, say, talk (141)

lūdus, lūdī (m.) - game, play, school (3)

lūna, lūnae (f.) - moon (99)

lūx, lūcis (f.) - light (85); prīmā lūce - at daybreak (85)

m

magister, magistrī (m.) - master, teacher, director (7)

magnopere - *adv.*, greatly (13)

magnus, magna, magnum - *adj.*, large, great, loud; much (when referring to money) (11); magna pars - majority, greater part (97)

male - *adv.*, badly, insufficiently (7)

malus, mala, malum - *adj.*, bad, evil (11)

maneō, manēre, mānsī, mānsum - stay, remain (5)

manus, manūs (f.) - hand, band (of men) (7)

APPENDIX

Latin - English Glossary

mare, maris (n.) - sea (7)

māter, mātris (f.) - mother (7)

māteria, māteriae (f.) - material, subject matter, lumber (143)

maximē - *adv.*, most, most greatly, especially (13)

mē - *personal pro. (acc.)*, me; *(abl.)*, with/by/from me (71)

mediā nocte - at midnight (90)

medicus, medicī (m.) - doctor, physician (11)

mediē - *adv.*, moderately

medius, media, medium - *adj.*, middle of (9); mediā nocte - at midnight (90)

meī - *personal pro. (gen.)*, of me (71)

memoria, memoriae (f.) - memory (5); memoriā teneō - remember (13)

memoriā teneō - remember (13)

mēns, mentis (f.) - mind, thought (117)

mēnsa, mēnsae (f.) - table, course (11); secunda mēnsa - dessert (13)

meus, mea, meum - *possessive adj.*, my, mine (9)

mihi - *personal pro. (dat.)*, to/for me (71)

mīlle - *cardinal num.*, one thousand (M) (77)

mīllēsimus, -a, -um - *ordinal num.*, one thousandth (79)

miser, misera, miserum - *adj.*, unhappy, wretched, unfortunate, poor (9)

miserē - *adv.*, wretchedly, desperately

mittō, mittere, mīsī, missum - send, let go (5)

moneō, monēre, monuī, monitum - warn, advise, inform (5)

mōns, montis (m.) - mountain, hill (97)

moror, morārī, morātus sum - *dep.*, delay (139)

mors, mortis (f.) - death (7)

mōs, mōris (m.) - custom, habit; (pl., habits, character) (83)

moveō, movēre, mōvī, mōtum - move, affect (5); castra ... moveō - break camp (13)

mox - *adv.*, soon (45)

multā nocte - late at night (13)

multitūdō, multitūdinis (f.) - great number, crowd (11)

multō diē - late in the day (13)

multus, multa, multum - *adj.*, much (11); (pl., many) (9); ad multam noctem - until late at night (13); multā nocte - late at night (13); multō diē - late in the day (13)

mūrus, mūrī (m.) - wall (11)

n

nam - *conj.*, for (7)

nārrō, nārrāre, nārrāvī, nārrātum - relate, tell (5)

nātūra, nātūrae (f.) - nature (5)

nauta, nautae (m.) - sailor (5)

nāvigō, nāvigāre, nāvigāvī, nāvigātum - sail (5)

nāvis, nāvis (f.) - ship (61); nāvis longa - battleship (13)

nāvis longa - battleship (13)

nec - *conj.*, and ... not, nor, neither (13)

necesse - *defective adj. (nom. and acc. sing only; takes being verb; often with dat.)*, necessary, inevitable (121)

neque - *conj.*, and ... not, nor, neither (13)

neque ... neque - neither ... nor (13)

niger, nigra, nigrum - *adj.*, black (89)

nihil (n.) - *defective noun (lacks gen., dat., abl. sing. and all pl. forms)*, nothing (83)

nīl (n.) - *defective noun (lacks gen., dat., abl. sing. and all pl. forms)*, nothing (83)

nōbīs - *personal pro. (dat.)*, to/for us; *(abl.)*, with/by/from us (71)

nōlō, nōlle, nōluī - *(when used with infinitive, subj. of infinitive must be acc. case)*, not wish, be unwilling (67, 197)

nōlumus - *1st person pl. of* nōlō (197)

nōlunt - *3rd person pl. of* nōlō (197)

nōmen, nōminis (n.) - name (7)

nōn - *adv.*, not (7)

nōn sōlum ... sed etiam - not only ... but also (13)

nōn vīs - *2nd person sing. of* nōlō (197)

nōn vult - *3rd person sing. of* nōlō (197)

nōn vultis - *2nd person pl. of* nōlō (197)

nōndum - *adv.*, not yet (13)

nōnus, -a, -um - *ordinal num.*, ninth (79)

APPENDIX

Latin - English Glossary

nōs - *personal pro. (nom.)*, we; *(acc.)*, us (71)

noster, nostra, nostrum - *possessive adj.*, our, ours (9)

nostrī - *possessive adj.*; *personal pro. (gen.)*, of us (71)

nostrum - *possessive adj.*; *personal pro. (gen.)*, of us (71)

novē - *adv.*, newly (47)

novem - *cardinal num.*, nine (IX) (77)

novus, nova, novum - *adj.*, new (47); **rēs novae** - revolution (95)

nox, noctis (f.) - night (7); **ad multam noctem** - until late at night (13); **mediā nocte** - at midnight (90); **multā nocte** - late at night (13); **prīmā nocte** - early in the night (86)

numerus, numerī (m.) - number, group (5)

numquam - *adv.*, never (13)

nunc - *adv.*, now (7)

nūntiō, nūntiāre, nūntiāvī, nūntiātum - announce, report (5)

nūntius, nūntī (m.) - messenger, message, news (5)

o

ob - *prep. (with acc.)*, because of, on account of, for the purpose of (7)

occupō, occupāre, occupāvī, occupātum - seize, capture (11)

octāvus, -a, -um - *ordinal num.*, eighth (79)

octō - *cardinal num.*, eight (VIII) (77)

oculus, oculī (m.) - eye (83)

officium, officī (n.) - duty (101)

ōlim - *adv.*, once, formerly, at that time, some day (137)

omnis, omne - *adj.*, every, all; (pl., everyone, everything) (11)

oportet - *impersonal verb (takes acc. and often infinitive)*, it is necessary, it is proper (63)

oppidum, oppidī (n.) - town (11)

oppugnō, oppugnāre, oppugnāvī, oppugnātum - attack (11)

opus, operis (n.) - work, deed, workmanship (121)

ōrātiō, ōrātiōnis (f.) - speech (11); **ōrātiōnem habeō** - deliver a speech (13)

ōrātiōnem habeō - deliver a speech (13)

p

pānis, pānis (m.) - bread, loaf (11)

parātē - *adv.*, carefully, promptly, readily (63)

parātus, parāta, parātum - *adj.*, ready, prepared (63)

parō, parāre, parāvī, parātum - prepare, prepare for (5)

pars, partis (f.) - part, share, direction (97); **magna pars** - majority, greater part (97)

parvus, parva, parvum - *adj.*, small, little (11)

pater, patris (m.) - father (9); (pl., senators) (11)

patria, patriae (f.) - country, native land (3)

paucī, paucae, pauca - *adj. (followed by* dē *or* ex *and the abl. of place from which to express the partitive idea)*, few, a few (95)

pāx, pācis (f.) - peace (103)

pecūnia, pecūniae (f.) - wealth, money (9)

per - *prep. (with acc.)*, through, across, by, by means of (11)

perficiō, perficere, perfēcī, perfectum - finish, accomplish, complete (5)

perīculum, perīculī (n.) - danger, risk (11)

perveniō, pervenīre, pervēnī, perventum - *(takes acc. of place to which)*, reach, arrive at (87)

pēs, pedis (m.) - foot (89)

plēnē - *adv.*, fully, completely (49)

plēnus, plēna, plēnum - *adj.*, full (49)

poena, poenae (f.) - penalty, punishment (3)

poēta, poētae (m.) - poet (3)

pōnō, pōnere, posuī, positum - put, set, place, locate (5)

pōns, pontis (m.) - bridge (145)

populus, populī (m.) - people, nation, tribe (9)

porta, portae (f.) - gate (3)

portō, portāre, portāvī, portātum - carry (5)

portus, portūs (m.) - harbor, port (9)

possum, posse, potuī - *(takes infinitive)*, can, be able (53, 195)

possumus - *1st person pl. of* **possum** (195)

APPENDIX

Latin - English Glossary

possunt - *3rd person pl. of* possum (195)

post - *prep. (with acc.)*, behind (referring to a place), after (referring to time) (11)

posteā - *adv.*, after that time, afterward, thereafter (7)

potēns (*genitive:* potentis) - *adj.*, powerful (11)

potenter - *adv.*, powerfully

potes - *2nd person sing. of* possum (195)

potest - *3rd person sing. of* possum (195)

potestās, potestātis (f.) - power, opportunity (9)

potestis - *2nd person pl. of* possum (195)

praemium, praemī (n.) - reward (11)

prīmā aestāte - at the beginning of summer (86)

prīmā lūce - at daybreak (85)

prīmā nocte - early in the night (86)

prīmus, prīma, prīmum - *ordinal num.*, first (79); **prīmā aestāte** - at the beginning of summer (86); **prīmā lūce** - at daybreak (85); **prīmā nocte** - early in the night (86)

prīncipium, prīncipī (n.) - beginning, origin (125)

prō - *prep. (with abl.)*, in front of, for, before, on behalf of, instead of (81)

probō, probāre, probāvī, probātum - prove, approve of, test (121)

proelium, proelī (n.) - battle (9)

prohibeō, prohibēre, prohibuī, prohibitum - (*may take objective infinitive*), prevent, hold back, keep ... from (51)

propter - *prep. (with acc.)*, because of, on account of (59)

prōvincia, prōvinciae (f.) - province (3)

prūdēns (*genitive:* prūdentis) - *adj.*, foresighted, wise, prudent (11)

prūdenter - *adv.*, wisely, prudently (11)

pūblicē - *adv.*, publicly, officially (95)

pūblicus, pūblica, pūblicum - *adj.*, public, belonging to the people (95); **rēs pūblica** - state, government, republic (95)

puella, puellae (f.) - girl (3)

puer, puerī (m.) - boy (3)

pugna, pugnae (f.) - fight (123)

pugnō, pugnāre, pugnāvī, pugnātum - fight (5)

pulcher, pulchra, pulchrum - *adj.*, beautiful, noble, fine (9)

pulchrē - *adv.*, beautifully, nobly

putō, putāre, putāvī, putātum - think (103)

q

quā dē causā - for which reason (13)

quārtus, -a, -um - *ordinal num.*, fourth (79)

quārtus decimus - *ordinal num.*, fourteenth (79)

quattuor - *cardinal num.*, four (IV) (77)

quattuordecim - *cardinal num.*, fourteen (XIV) (77)

quid - *interrogative adv.*, what? (7)

quīndecim - *cardinal num.*, fifteen (XV) (77)

quīnque - *cardinal num.*, five (V) (77)

quīntus, -a, -um - *ordinal num.*, fifth (79)

quīntus decimus - *ordinal num.*, fifteenth (79)

quod - *conj.*, because (7)

quōmodo - *interrogative adv.*, how? (7)

r

rapiō, rapere, rapuī, raptum - seize, snatch (11)

reddō, reddere, reddidī, redditum - give back, restore (11)

rēgina, rēgīnae (f.) - queen (5)

rēgnō, rēgnāre, rēgnāvī, rēgnātum - reign, dominate (45)

regō, regere, rēxī, rēctum - rule (11)

relinquō, relinquere, relīquī, relictum - leave, leave behind (11)

reliquus, reliqua, reliquum - *adj.*, remaining, the rest of (99)

reperiō, reperīre, repperī, repertum - find, discover (11)

rēs, reī (f.) - thing, matter, affair (95); **rēs novae** - revolution (95); **rēs pūblica** - state, government, republic (95)

rēs novae - revolution (95)

rēs pūblica - state, government, republic (95)

APPENDIX

Latin - English Glossary

respondeō, respondēre, respondī, respōnsum - answer, reply (11)

retineō, retinēre, retinuī, retentum - hold back (11)

rēx, rēgis (m.) - king (5)

S

sacer, sacra, sacrum - *adj.*, sacred, holy; (neuter pl., religious ceremonies, rituals) (11)

saepe - *adv.*, often (7)

salūs, salūtis (f.) - safety, welfare, greeting (119)

sciō, scīre, scīvī, scītum - know (9)

scrībō, scrībere, scrīpsī, scrīptum - write (5)

secunda mēnsa - dessert (13)

secundus, -a, -um - *ordinal num.*, second (79); secunda mēnsa - dessert (13)

sed - *conj.*, but (7)

sēdecim - *cardinal num.*, sixteen (XVI) (77)

sedeō, sedēre, sēdī, sessum - sit (5)

sella, sellae (f.) - chair, seat (9)

semper - *adv.*, always (7)

senātus, senātūs (m.) - senate (9)

septem - *cardinal num.*, seven (VII) (77)

septendecim - *cardinal num.*, seventeen (XVII) (77)

septimus, -a, -um - *ordinal num.*, seventh (79)

septimus decimus - *ordinal num.*, seventeenth (79)

servō, servāre, servāvī, servātum - guard, save, keep (5)

servus, servī (m.) - slave (3)

sex - *cardinal num.*, six (VI) (77)

sextus, -a, -um - *ordinal num.*, sixth (79)

sextus decimus - *ordinal num.*, sixteenth (79)

signum, signī (n.) - sign, signal (139)

silva, silvae (f.) - forest (3)

similis, simile - *adj.*, *(used with dat.)*, like, similar (11)

similiter - *adv.*, in like manner, similarly

simul atque - as soon as (13)

sine - *prep. (with abl.)*, without (11)

sinister, sinistra, sinistrum - *adj.*, left, left-hand (9); ā sinistrō cornū - on the left wing (13)

sinistrē - *adv.*, badly, wrongly

socius, socī (m.) - comrade, ally (3)

sōl, sōlis (m.) - sun (101)

soror, sorōris (f.) - sister (9)

spectō, spectāre, spectāvī, spectātum - look at (5)

spērō, spērāre, spērāvī, spērātum - *(used in indirect statement, usu. with fut. act. infinitive)*, hope (89)

spēs, speī (f.) - hope (9)

spīrō, spīrāre, spīrāvī, spīrātum - breathe, blow, exhale (85)

statim - *adv.*, immediately, at once (11)

stella, stellae (f.) - star (117)

stō, stāre, stetī, stātum - stand (5)

studium, studī (n.) - eagerness, zeal, enthusiasm (143)

sub - *prep. (with acc.)*, close under, under, close to, up to, to the foot of; *prep. (with abl.)*, at the foot of, under, close to (11)

sum, esse, fuī, futūrus - *(the "being" verb)* (24, 194)

summē - *adv.*, very, intensely, extremely (47)

summus, summa, summum - *adj.*, highest, top of, greatest, chief (47)

sumus - *1st person pl. of* sum (24)

sunt - *3rd person pl. of* sum (24); - they are, there are (9)

super - *prep. (with acc.)*, over, above (11)

superō, superāre, superāvī, superātum - surpass, defeat (5)

surgō, surgere, surrēxī, surrēctum - rise, stand up (9)

t

tamen - *conj.*, *postpositive*, nevertheless, still, yet (7)

tē - *personal pro. (acc. sing.)*, you; *(abl. sing.)*, with/by/from you (71)

tēlum, tēlī (n.) - offensive weapon, missile (145)

temptō, temptāre, temptāvī, temptātum - try, attempt (11)

tempus, temporis (n.) - time (61); brevī tempore - in a short time, soon (13)

teneō, tenēre, tenuī, tentum - hold (11); memoriā teneō - remember (13)

terra, terrae (f.) - earth, land, country (7)

APPENDIX

Latin - English Glossary

terreō, terrēre, terruī, territum - frighten (11)

tertius, -a, -um - *ordinal num.*, third (79)

tertius decimus - *ordinal num.*, thirteenth (79)

tibi - *personal pro. (dat. sing.)*, to/for you (71)

timeō, timēre, timuī, (-) - fear, be afraid (81)

timor, timōris (m.) - fear (83)

trādō, trādere, trādidī, trāditum - hand over, surrender, hand down (11)

trahō, trahere, trāxī, tractum - draw, drag, lead (145)

trāns - *prep. (with acc.)*, across, over (11)

tredecim - *cardinal num.*, thirteen (XIII) (77)

trēs, tria - *cardinal num.*, three (III) (77)

trīstis, trīste - *adj.*, sad, grim (11)

trīstiter - *adv.*, (to cry) bitterly

tū - *personal pro. (nom.)*, you (sing.) (71)

tuba, tubae (f.) - trumpet (7)

tuī - *personal pro. (gen. sing.)*, of you (71)

tum - *adv.*, then, at that time (7)

tuus, tua, tuum - *possessive adj.*, your, yours (singular) (9)

U

ubi - *interrogative adv.*, where? (7); *relative adv.*, where, when (13)

ūndecim - *cardinal num.*, eleven (XI) (77)

ūndecimus, -a, -um - *ordinal num.*, eleventh (79)

ūndēvīcēsimus, -a, -um - *ordinal num.*, nineteenth (79)

ūndēvīgintī - *cardinal num.*, nineteen (XIX) (77)

ūnus, ūna, ūnum - *cardinal num.*, one (I) (77)

urbs, urbis (f.) - city (3)

ūsque - *adv.*, all the way, all the time, even (117)

V

validē - *adv.*, strongly

validus, valida, validum - *adj.*, strong (13)

vēndō, vēndere, vēndidī, vēnditum - sell (137)

veniō, venīre, vēnī, ventum - come (5)

ventus, ventī (m.) - wind (119)

verbum, verbī (n.) - word (3)

vērē - *adv.*, really, truly (53)

vereor, verērī, veritus sum - *dep.*, fear, respect (137)

vēritās, vēritātis (f.) - truth, trueness (3)

vērus, vēra, vērum - *adj.*, true (53)

vester, vestra, vestrum - *possessive adj.*, your, yours (plural) (9)

vestrī - *possessive adj.*; *personal pro. (gen. pl.)*, of you (71)

vestrum - *possessive adj.*; *personal pro. (gen. pl.)*, of you (71)

via, viae (f.) - road, way, street (3)

vīcēsimus, -a, -um - *ordinal num.*, twentieth (79)

victōria, victōriae (f.) - victory (137)

videō, vidēre, vīdī, vīsum - see (5)

vīgintī - *cardinal num.*, twenty (XX) (77)

vīlla, vīllae (f.) - farmhouse, country house, villa (3)

vincō, vincere, vīcī, victum - conquer, defeat, be victorious, win (5)

vir, virī (m.) - man, husband, hero (3)

virtūs, virtūtis (f.) - manliness, courage, virtue (125)

vīs - *2nd person sing. of* volō (196)

vīta, vītae (f.) - life (3)

vīvō, vīvere, vīxī, vīctum - live, be alive (125)

vōbīs - *personal pro. (dat. pl.)*, to/for you; *(abl. pl.)*, with/by/from you (71)

vocō, vocāre, vocāvī, vocātum - call (5)

volō, velle, voluī - *(when used with infinitive, subj. of infinitive must be acc. case)*, wish, want, be willing (67, 196)

volō, volāre, volāvī, volātum - fly (5)

volumus - *1st person pl. of* volō (196)

volunt - *3rd person pl. of* volō (196)

vōs - *personal pro. (nom. pl.)*, you; *(acc. pl.)*, you (71)

vōx, vōcis (f.) - voice (51)

vulnerō, vulnerāre, vulnerāvī, vulnerātum - wound (5)

vulnus, vulneris (n.) - wound (99)

vult - *3rd person sing. of* volō (196)

vultis - *2nd person pl. of* volō (196)

APPENDIX

English - Latin Glossary

a

a few - paucī
able (be) - possum
about - dē *(with abl.)*
above - super *(with acc.)*
accept - accipiō
accomplish - perficiō
across - per *(with acc.)*;
    trāns *(with acc.)*
address - appellō
advice - cōnsilium
advise - moneō
affair - rēs
affect - moveō
after (referring to time) - post
    (with acc.)
after that time - posteā
afterward - posteā
against - contrā *(with acc.)*; in
    (with acc.)
all - omnis
all the time - ūsque
all the way - ūsque
ally - socius
along with - cum *(with abl.)*
already - iam
also - et, etiam
always - semper
am - sum
am alive - vīvō
am hard pressed - labōrō
am under an obligation - grātiam
    dēbeō
am unwilling - nōlō
am willing - volō
ambassador - lēgātus
among - inter *(with acc.)*
ancient - antīquus
and - atque, et

and also - atque
and even - atque
and ... not - nec, neque
and so - itaque
anger - īra
animal - animal
announce - nūntiō
answer - respondeō
anxiety - cūra
appoint a day - diem cōnstituō
approach - adventus
approve of - probō
arms - arma
arrival - adventus
arrive at - perveniō
as - atque
as long as - dum
as soon as - simul atque
assemble - convocō
at - ad *(with acc.)*
at daybreak - prīmā lūce
at midnight - mediā nocte
at once - statim
at that time - ōlim, tum
at the beginning of summer
    - prīmā aestāte
at the foot of - sub *(with abl.)*
attack - oppugnō
attempt - cōnor, temptō
aught - dēbeō
avoid - fugiō
await - exspectō
awareness - cōnscientia
away from - ā, ab *(with abl.)*

b

bad - malus
badly - male, sinistrē
baggage - impedīmenta

band (of men) - manus
battle - proelium
battleship - nāvis longa
be able - possum
be afraid - timeō
be mistaken - errō
be victorious - vincō
bear - gerō
beautiful - pulcher
beautifully - pulchrē
because - quod
because of - ob *(with acc.)*;
    propter *(with acc.)*
bed - lectus
before - ante *(with acc.)*;
    prō *(with abl.)*
begin - incipiō
beginning - prīncipium
behind (referring to a place) - post
    (with acc.)
behold - ecce
believe - crēdō
belonging to the people - pūblicus
benefit - beneficium
between - inter *(with acc.)*
bid - iubeō
bird - avis
bitterly (to cry) - trīstiter
black - niger
blow - spīrō
body - corpus
bold - audāx
boldly - audācter
boldness - audācia
book - liber
both ... and - et ... et
boy - puer
brave - fortis
bravely - fortiter

APPENDIX

English - Latin Glossary

bread - pānis
break camp - castra ... moveō
breathe - spīrō
bridge - pōns
brief - brevis
briefly - breviter
bright - clārus
brightly - clārē
bring - dūcō
broad - lātus
brother - frāter
but - sed
by - ā, ab *(with abl.)*;
    per *(with acc.)*
by far - longē
by her *(abl.)* - eā
by him *(abl.)* - eō
by it *(abl.)* - eō
by me *(abl.)* - mē
by means of - per *(with acc.)*
by them (m. or f. or n.) *(abl.)* - eīs
by us *(abl.)* - nōbīs
by you (pl.) *(abl.)* - vōbīs;
    (s.) *(abl.)* - tē

c

call - appellō, vocō
call together - convocō
can - possum
captive - captīvus
capture - capiō, occupō
care - cūra, dīligentia
carefully - parātē
carry - portō
carry on - gerō
cart - carrus
cause - causa
certain - certus
certainly - certē

chair - sella
chance - fortūna
character - mōrēs
chief - summus
children - līberī
choose - dēligō
citizen - cīvis
city - urbs
clan - gēns
clear - clārus
clearly - clārē
close - claudō
close to - sub *(with acc.)*;
    sub *(with abl.)*
close under - sub *(with acc.)*
collect - cōgō
come - veniō
come upon - inveniō
command - iubeō
compel - cōgō
complete - perficiō
completely - plēnē
comrade - socius
concerning - dē *(with abl.)*
confidence - fidēs
conquer - vincō
conscience - cōnscientia
consider - cōgitō, habeō, iūdicō
country - patria, terra
country house - vīlla
courage - animī, virtūs
course - mēnsa
crowd - multitūdō
(cry) bitterly - trīstiter
cultivated - hūmānus
custom - mōs

d

daily - cotīdiē

danger - perīculum
dare - audeō
daring - audācia, audāx
daughter - fīlia
day - diēs
death - mors
deceptive - falsus
decide - cōnstituō
declare - cōnfirmō
deed - opus
deep - altus
deeply - altē, graviter
defeat - superō, vincō
defend - dēfendō
defensive arms - arma
delay - moror
deliver a speech - ōrātiōnem
    habeō
departure - exitus
desire - cupiō
desperately - miserē
dessert - secunda mēnsa
determine - cōnstituō
difficulty - labor
diligence - dīligentia
diligent - certus
dining couch - lectus
dinner - cēna
direction - pars
director - magister
discern - cernō
discover - reperiō
distinguish - cernō
do - agō, faciō
do good to - iuvō
doctor - medicus
dominate - rēgnō
door - iānua
doubt - dubitō

APPENDIX

English - Latin Glossary

doubtful - incertus
down from - dē *(with abl.)*
drag - trahō
draw - trahō
drink - bibō
drive - agō
duty - officium
dwell - habitō

e

eagerness - studium
early in the night - prīmā nocte
earth - terra
easy - facilis
eat - edō
eight (VIII) - octō
eighteen (XVIII) - duodēvīnginti
eighteenth - duodēvīcēsimus
eighth - octāvus
either ... or - aut ... aut
eleven (XI) - ūndecim
eleventh - ūndecimus
encourage - cōnfirmō
end - exitus
enemy (of the State) - hostis;
    (personal) - inimīcus
enthusiasm - studium
envoy - lēgātus
epistle - epistula, litterae
err - errō
especially - maximē
establish - cōnstituō
even - et, etiam, ūsque
every - omnis
every day - cotīdiē
everyone - omnēs
everything - omnēs
evil - malus
exhale - spīrō

exile - fuga
extremely - summē
eye - oculus

f

faith - fidēs
faithful - fidēlis
faithfully - fidēliter
false - falsus
falsely - falsē
fame - laus
family - gēns
famous - clārus
famously - clārē
far - longē
far off - longē
farmer - agricola
farmhouse - vīlla
father - pater
favor - beneficium, grātia
fear - timeō, timor, vereor
feel gratitude - grātiam habeō
feigned - falsus
few - paucī
field - ager, campus
fierce - ācer
fiercely - ācriter
fifteen (XV) - quīndecim
fifteenth - quīntus decimus
fifth - quīntus
fight - pugna, pugnō
find - inveniō, reperiō
fine - pulcher
finish - perficiō
fire - ignis
first - prīmus
five (V) - quīnque
flee - fugiō
flee from - fugiō

flight - fuga
flower - flōs
flowing - flūmen
fly - volō
food - cibus
foot - pēs
for - ad *(with acc.)*; in *(with acc.)*;
    nam; prō *(with abl.)*
for a long time - diū
for her *(dat.)* - eī
for him *(dat.)* - eī
for it *(dat.)* - eī
for me *(dat.)* - mihi
for the purpose of - ob *(with acc.)*
for them (m. or f. or n.) *(dat.)* - eīs
for us *(dat.)* - nōbīs
for which reason - quā dē causā
for you (pl.) *(dat.)* - vōbīs;
    (s.) *(dat.)* - tibi
forces - cōpiae
foresight - cōnsilium
foresighted - prūdēns
forest - silva
form (make) a plan - cōnsilium
    capiō
former - antiquus
formerly - ōlim
fortunate - fēlix
fortunately - fēlīciter
fortune - fortūna
forum - forum
four (IV) - quattuor
fourteen (XIV) - quattuordecim
fourteenth - quārtus decimus
fourth - quārtus
free - liber, līberō
freedom - lībertās
friend - amīcus
friendliness - amīcitia

APPENDIX

English - Latin Glossary

friendly - amīcus
friendship - amīcitia
frighten - terreō
from - ā, ab *(with abl.)*; dē *(with abl.)*; ē, ex *(with abl.)*
from her *(abl.)* - eā
from him *(abl.)* - eō
from it *(abl.)* - eō
from me *(abl.)* - mē
from them (m. or f. or n.) *(abl.)* - eīs
from us *(abl.)* - nōbīs
from you (pl.) *(abl.)* - vōbīs
from you (s.) *(abl.)* - tē
full - plēnus
fully - bene, plēnē

g
game - lūdus
garden - hortus
gate - porta
gently - hūmānē
gift - dōnum
girl - puella
give - dō
give back - reddō
give thanks - grātiās agō
give way - cēdō
glad - laetus
gladly - laetē
gladness - gaudium
go out - excēdō
god - deus
good - bonus
good luck - fēlīcitās
govern - gubernō
government - rēs pūblica
grain - frūmentum
grant - dō

grass - herba
gratefully - grātē
gratitude - grātia
great - magnus
great number - multitūdō
greater part - magna pars
greatest - summus
greatly - magnopere
greeting - salūs
grievously - graviter
grim - trīstis
group - numerus
guard - servō
guide - dux

h
habit - mōs
habits - mōrēs
hand - manus
hand down - trādō
hand over - trādō
happily - fēlīciter, laetē
happy - fēlix, laetus
harbor - portus
have - habeō
he *(nom.)* - is
he can - potest
he does not wish - nōn vult
he is - est
he is able - potest
he is unwilling - nōn vult
he is willing - vult
he says - inquit
he wants - vult
he wishes - vult
head - caput
hear - audiō
heavens - caelum
heavily - graviter

heavy - gravis
help - iuvō
her *(acc.)* - eam; *(gen.)* - eius
hero - vir
hesitate - dubitō
high - altus
highest - summus
hill - mōns
him *(acc.)* - eum
hinder - impediō
hindrance - impedīmentum
his *(gen.)* - eius
hold - habeō, teneō
hold back - prohibeō, retineō
holy - sacer
hope - spērō, spēs
horn - cornū
horse - equus
hostile - inimīcus
hour - hōra
how? - quōmodo
human - hūmānus
human being - homō
husband - vir

i
I *(nom.)* - ego
immediately - statim
impede - impediō
impediment - impedīmentum
in - in *(with abl.)*
in a friendly way - amīcē
in a short time - brevī tempore, brevī
in former times - antīquē
in front of - ante *(with acc.)*; prō *(with abl.)*
in like manner - similiter
in that place - ibi

APPENDIX

English - Latin Glossary

in the rear - ā tergō
inevitable - necesse
influence - grātia
inform - doceō, moneō
injury - iniūria
injustice - iniūria
instead of - prō *(with abl.)*
insufficiently - male
insult - iniūria
intensely - summē
into - in *(with acc.)*
island - īnsula
it can - potest
it does not wish - nōn vult
it is - est
it is able - potest
it is necessary - oportet
it is permitted - licet
it is proper - oportet
it is unwilling - nōn vult
it is willing - vult
it says - inquit
it wants - vult
it wishes - vult
its *(gen.)* - eius

j
join - iungō
journey - iter
joy - gaudium
joyful - laetus
joyfully - laetē
judge - iūdex, iūdicō
juror - iūdex
justice - iūs

k
keep - habeō, servō
keep ... from - prohibeō

kill - interficiō
kindness - beneficium
king - rēx
know - sciō
knowledge - cōnscientia

l
labor - labor, labōrō
lack - inopia
land - terra
language - lingua
large - magnus
late at night - multā nocte
late in the day - multō diē
law - iūs, lēx
lead - dūcō, trahō
leader - dux
leave - excēdō, relinquō
leave behind - relinquō
left - sinister
left-hand - sinister
let go - mittō
letter - epistula, litterae
letter (of the alphabet) - littera
liberty - lībertās
lieutenant - lēgātus
life - vīta
light - lūx
like - amō, similis *(with dat.)*
listen to - audiō
little - parvus
live - habitō, vīvō
loaf - pānis
locate - pōnō
location - locus
long - diū; (referring to space), longus
look at - spectō
lord - dominus

lose - āmittō
loud - magnus
love - amō
loyal - fidēlis
loyally - fidēliter
loyalty - fidēs
luck - fortūna
lucky - fēlix
lumber - māteria

m
majority - magna pars
make - faciō
make (form) a plan - cōnsilium capiō
man - homō, vir
manliness - virtūs
many - multī
march - iter, iter faciō
marketplace - forum
master - dominus, magister
material - māteria
matter - rēs
me *(acc.)* - mē
meanwhile - interim
memory - memoria
message - nūntius
messenger - nūntius
middle of - medius
mind - animus, mēns
mine - meus
missile - tēlum
moderately - mediē
money - pecūnia
moon - lūna
most - maximē
most greatly - maximē
mother - māter
mountain - mōns

APPENDIX

English - Latin Glossary

move - cēdō, moveō
much - multus; (when referring to money), magnus
my - meus

n

name - appellō, nōmen
nation - gēns, populus
native land - patria
nature - nātūra
navigate - gubernō
near - ad *(with acc.)*
necessary (be) - necesse
need - inopia
neither - nec, neque
neither ... nor - neque ... neque
never - numquam
nevertheless - tamen
new - novus
newly - novē
news - nūntius
night - nox
nine (IX) - novem
nineteen (XIX) - ūndēvīgintī
nineteenth - ūndēvīcēsimus
ninth - nōnus
noble - pulcher
nobly - pulchrē
noise - clāmor
nor - nec, neque
not - nōn
not only ... but also
      - nōn sōlum ... sed etiam
not wish - nōlō
not yet - nōndum
nothing - nīl, nihil
now - iam, nunc
number - numerus

o

of - dē *(with abl.)*; ē, ex *(with abl.)*
of her (her) *(gen.)* - eius
of him (his) *(gen.)* - eius
of it (its) *(gen.)* - eius
of me *(gen.)* - meī
of them (their) (f.) *(gen.)* - eārum; (m. or n.) *(gen.)* - eōrum
of us *(gen.)* - nostrī, nostrum
of you (pl.) *(gen.)* - vestrī, vestrum; (s.) *(gen.)* - tuī
offensive weapon - tēlum
officially - pūblicē
often - saepe
old - antīquus
on - in *(with abl.)*
on account of - ob *(with acc.)*; propter *(with acc.)*
on behalf of - prō *(with abl.)*
on high - altē
on the left wing - ā sinistrō cornū
on the right - ā dextrā
on the right wing - ā dextrō cornū
once - ōlim
one (I) - ūnus
one hundred (C) - centum
one hundredth - centēsimus
one thousand (M) - mīlle
one thousandth - mīllēsimus
onto - in *(with acc.)*
opportunity - potestās
opposite - contrā *(with acc.)*
or - aut
order - iubeō
origin - prīncipium
our - noster
ours - noster
out of - ē, ex *(with abl.)*
outcome - exitus

over - in *(with abl.)*; super *(with acc.)*; trāns *(with acc.)*
owe - dēbeō
owner - dominus

p

part - pars
peace - pāx
penalty - poena
people - populus
permitted (it is) - licet
physician - medicus
place - locus, pōnō
plain - campus
plan - cōgitō, cōnsilium
play - lūdus
pleasantly - grātē
please - dēlectō
pleasing - grātus
pledge - fidēs
plenty - cōpia
poem - carmen
poet - poēta
point out - dēmōnstrō
politely - hūmānē
poor - miser
port - portus
poverty - inopia
power - potestās
powerful - potēns
powerfully - potenter
praise - laudō, laus
prepare - parō
prepare for - parō
prepared - parātus
present - dōnum
prevent - impediō, prohibeō
prisoner - captīvus
promptly - parātē

English - Latin Glossary

proper (it is) - oportet
prosperity - fēlicitās
prove - probō
province - prōvincia
prudent - prūdēns
prudently - prūdenter
public - pūblicus
publicly - pūblicē
punishment - poena
put - pōnō

q

queen - rēgīna
quick - celer
quickly - celeriter

r

rashly - audācter
reach - perveniō
readily - parātē
ready - parātus
really - vērē
reason - causa
receive - accipiō
refined - hūmānus
regard - habeō
reign - rēgnō
relate - nārrō
reliable - certus
religious ceremonies - sacra
remain - maneō
remaining - reliquus
remember - memoriā teneō
reply - respondeō
report - fāma, nūntiō
republic - rēs pūblica
reputation - fāma
respect - vereor
rest of - reliquus

restore - reddō
revolution - rēs novae
reward - praemium
right - dexter, iūs
right-hand - dexter
rise - surgō
risk - perīculum
rituals - sacra
river - flūmen
road - via
route - iter
rule - regō
rumor - fāma
run - currō

s

sacred - sacer
sad - trīstis
safety - salūs
sail - nāvigō
sailor - nauta
save - servō
say - dīcō, inquam, loquor
school - lūdus
sea - mare
seat - sella
second - secundus
see - videō
seize - occupō, rapiō
sell - vēndō
senate - senātus
senators - patrēs
send - mittō
serious - gravis
seriously - graviter
set - pōnō
set free - līberō
set up - cōnstituō
seven (VII) - septem

seventeen (XVII) - septendecim
seventeenth - septimus decimus
seventh - septimus
severe - gravis
severely - graviter
share - pars
sharp - ācer
sharply - ācriter
she (nom.) - ea
she can - potest
she does not wish - nōn vult
she is - est
she is able - potest
she is unwilling - nōn vult
she is willing - vult
she says - inquit
she wants - vult
she wishes - vult
ship - nāvis
short - brevis
shout - clāmō, clāmor
show - doceō, dēmōnstrō
shut - claudō
sign - signum
signal - signum
similar - similis (with dat.)
similarly - similiter
sister - soror
sit - sedeō
situation - locus
six (VI) - sex
sixteen (XVI) - sēdecim
sixteenth - sextus decimus
sixth - sextus
skillfully - dexterē
sky - caelum
slave - servus
sleep - dormiō
small - parvus

APPENDIX

English - Latin Glossary

snatch - rapiō

some day - ōlim

son - filius

song - carmen

soon - brevī tempore, brevī, mox

speak - loquor

speech - ōrātiō

speedy - celer

spirit - animus

stand - stō

stand up - surgō

star - stella

state - rēs pūblica

stay - maneō

steer - gubernō

still - adhūc, tamen

stone - lapis

story - fābula

stream - flūmen

street - via

strengthen - cōnfirmō

stroll - ambulō

strong - validus

strongly - validē

subject matter - māteria

successfully - fēlīciter

suffer - labōrō

summer - aestās

summon - convocō

sun - sōl

supply - cōpia

sure - certus

surely - certē

surpass - superō

surrender - trādō

swift - celer

swiftly - celeriter

sword - gladius

t

table - mēnsa

take - capiō

talk - loquor

tall - altus

teach - doceō

teacher - magister

tell - dīcō, nārrō

ten (X) - decem

tenth - decimus

territory - ager

test - probō

thankful - grātus

the enemy - hostēs

their (m. or n.) (gen.) - eōrum

them (f.) (acc.) - eās; (m. or n.)
(acc.) - eōs; (n.) (acc.) - ea

then - ergō, tum

there - ibi

there are - sunt

there is - est

thereafter - posteā

therefore - ergō, itaque

they (f.) (nom.) - eae; (m.) (nom.)
- eī; (m. or n.) (nom.) - iī; (n.)
(nom.) - ea

they are - sunt

they are able - possunt

they are unwilling - nōlunt

they are willing - volunt

they can - possunt

they do not wish - nōlunt

they say - inquiunt

they want - volunt

they wish - volunt

thing - rēs

think - cōgitō, putō

third - tertius

thirteen (XIII) - tredecim

thirteenth - tertius decimus

thought - mēns

three (III) - trēs

through - per (with acc.)

throw - iaciō (with acc.)

time - tempus

tired - dēfessus

to - ad (with acc.)

to be - esse

to her (dat.) - eī

to him (dat.) - eī

to it (dat.) - eī

to me (dat.) - mihi

to the foot of - sub (with acc.)

to them (m. or f. or n.) (dat.) - eīs

to us (dat.) - nōbīs

to you (pl.) (dat.) - vōbīs; (s.) (dat.)
- tibi

today - hodiē

tomorrow - crās

tongue - lingua

top of - summus

toward - ad (with acc.); in (with
acc.)

town - oppidum

tree - arbor

tribe - populus

troops - cōpiae

true - vērus

trueness - vēritās

truly - vērē

trumpet - tuba

trust - crēdō

truth - vēritās

try - cōnor, temptō

twelfth - duodecimus

twelve (XII) - duodecim

twentieth - vīcēsimus

twenty (XX) - vīgintī

APPENDIX

English - Latin Glossary

two (II) - duo

u

uncertain - incertus
uncertainly - incertē
under - sub *(with acc.)*; sub *(with abl.)*
understand - cernō
unfortunate - miser
unfriendly - inimīcus
unhappy - miser
unsure - incertus
until - dum
until late at night - ad multam noctem
unwilling (be) - nōn vult
up to - sub *(with acc.)*
up to this time - adhūc
upon - in *(with abl.)*
us *(acc.)* - nōs

v

very - summē
victory - victōria
villa - vīlla
virtue - virtūs
voice - vōx

w

wage war - bellum gerō
wagon - carrus
wait for - exspectō
walk - ambulō
wall - mūrus
wander - errō
want - cupiō, inopia, volō
war - bellum
warn - moneō
wash - lavō

water - aqua
wave - fluctus
way - via
way out - exitus
we *(nom.)* - nōs
we are - sumus
we are able - possumus
we are unwilling - nōlumus
we are willing - volumus
we can - possumus
we do not wish - nōlumus
we want - volumus
we wish - volumus
wealth - pecūnia
weapons - arma
weapons for close fighting - arma
wear - gerō
weightily - graviter
welcome - grātus
welfare - salūs
well - bene
what? - quid
when - ubi
where - ubi
where? - ubi
while - dum
white - albus
why? - cūr
wide - lātus
widely - lātē
wife - fēmina
willing (be) - vult
willingly - grātē
win - vincō
wind - ventus
window - fenestra
wing (of an army) - cornū
winter - hiems
wise - prūdēns

wisely - prūdenter
wish - cupiō, volō
with - cum *(with abl.)*
with her *(abl.)* - eā
with him *(abl.)* - eō
with hostility - inimīcē
with it *(abl.)* - eō
with me *(abl.)* - mē
with them (m. or f. or n.) *(abl.)* - eīs
with us *(abl.)* - nōbīs
with you (pl.) *(abl.)* - vōbīs; (s.) *(abl.)* - tē
withdraw - cēdō
without - sine *(with abl.)*
woman - fēmina
word - verbum
work - labor, opus
workmanship - opus
wound - vulnerō, vulnus
wrath - īra
wretched - miser
wretchedly - miserē
write - scrībō
wrongly - sinistrē

y

year - annus
yesterday - herī
yet - tamen
yield - cēdō
you (pl) *(nom and acc.)* - vōs
you (s.) *(acc)* - tē; (s.) *(nom.)* - tū
you (pl.) are - estis
you (s.) are - es
you (pl.) are able - potestis
you (s.) are able - potes
you (pl.) are unwilling - nōn vultis
you (s.) are unwilling - nōn vīs

APPENDIX

English - Latin Glossary

you (pl.) are willing - vultis
you (s.) are willing - vīs
you (pl.) can - potestis
you (s.) can - potes
you (pl.) do not wish - nōn vultis
you (s.) do not wish - nōn vīs
you (s.) say - inquis
you (pl.) want - vultis
you (s.) want - vīs
you (pl.) wish - vultis
you (s.) wish - vīs
your (pl.) - vester; (s.) - tuus
yours (pl.) - vester; (s.) - tuus

Z
zeal - studium

APPENDIX

Latin Alphabet

Capital Letter	Small Letter	Pronunciation	Capital Letter	Small Letter	Pronunciation
Ā	ā	**a** in *father*	N	n	**n** in *nut*
A	a	**a** in *idea*	Ō**	ō**	**o** in *note*
B	b	**b** in *boy*	O**	o**	**o** in *omit*
C	c	**c** in *cat*	P	p	**p** in *pit*
D	d	**d** in *dog*	Q	q	**qu** in *quit*
Ē	ē	**ey** in *obey*	R	r	**r** in *run*
E	e	**e** in *bet*	S	s	**s** in *sit*
F	f	**f** in *fan*	T	t	**t** in *tag*
G	g	**g** in *go*	Ū	ū	**u** in *rule*
H	h	**h** in *hat*	U	u	**u** in *put*
Ī	ī	**i** in *machine*	V	v	**w** in *way*
I*	i*	**i** in *sit*	X	x	**ks** in *socks*
K	k	**k** in *king*	Ȳ	ȳ	form lips to say "**oo**" but say "**ee**" instead (held longer)
L	l	**l** in *land*	Y	y	form lips to say "**oo**" but say "**ee**" instead (held shorter)
M	m	**m** in *man*	Z	z	**dz** in *adze*

*When functioning as a consonant, **i** has the sound of **y** in *youth*. (See **Special Consonants** below.)

The **ō and the **o** both have a long o sound, but the **ō** is held longer.

Special Sounds

Diphthongs

Letters	Pronunciation
ae	*aye*
au	**ow** in *now*
ei	**ei** in *neighbor*
eu	*ay-oo*
oe	**oy** in *joy*
ui	**uee** in *queen*

Special Consonants

Letters	Pronunciation
bs	*ps*
bt	*pt*
ch	**ch** in *character*
gu	**gu** in *anguish*
i	**y** in *youth*
ph	**ph** in *phone*
su	**su** in *suave*
th	**th** in *thick*

APPENDIX

Macrons, Syllables, and Accents

I. **Rules for Macrons**

1. A vowel **always** has a macron before the letters -ns.
2. A vowel **never** has a macron before the letters -nt.
3. When the vowel -e- comes after another vowel, it has a macron.
4. When an -m, -r, or -t is the last letter in an ending added to a word, the vowel that comes before the -m, -r, or -t is **never** long.
5. If an -m, -r, or -t is the last letter in a word without an ending, the vowel that comes before the -m, -r, or -t is *almost* **never** long.

II. **Rules for Dividing Syllables**

1. When a consonant stands between two vowels or diphthongs, pronounce the consonant in the syllable with the second vowel or diphthong.
2. When two or more consonants stand between two vowels or diphthongs, pronounce only the last consonant in the syllable with the second vowel or diphthong. (Certain consonants like to stay together, such as h, l, or r coming after c, g, p, b, d, or t.)
3. When the consonant is a double consonant (x or z)*, place -x- with the vowel before, but -z- with the vowel after.
4. When the word is compound, separate the prefix from the rest of the word.

III. **Rules for Length of Syllables**

1. Syllables which are *long by nature*:
    a. A syllable is long by nature if it contains a long vowel (a vowel with a macron over it).
    b. A syllable is long by nature if it contains a diphthong.
2. Syllables which are *long by position*:
    a. A syllable is long by position if its vowel is followed by two or more consonants.
    b. A syllable is long by position if its vowel is followed by a double consonant (-x or -z).*

IV. **Rules of Accent**

1. On one syllable words, accent the ultima (the only syllable).
2. On two syllable words, accent the penult.
3. On three (or more) syllable words, accent the penult if it is long (by nature or by position). Accent the antepenult if the penult is short.

*The letters x and z are called double consonants because two sounds are needed to pronounce them. Pronounce the initial sound with the first syllable and the final sound with the second syllable.

APPENDIX

Principal Parts of the Latin Verb

Latin verbs generally have four main parts, called **principal parts**.

The Principal Parts of the Verb Amō

amō **Present System**	amāre **Present Infinitive**	amāvī **Perfect System**	amātum **Supine System**
present indicative (active & passive)	*present infinitive* (active & passive)	*perfect indicative* (active)	*perfect indicative* (passive)
imperfect indicative (active & passive)	*imperfect subjunctive* (active & passive)	*pluperfect indicative* (active)	*pluperfect indicative* (passive)
future indicative (active & passive)		*future perfect indicative* (active)	*future perfect indicative* (passive)
present participle (active)		*perfect infinitive* (active)	*perfect infinitive* (passive)
present subjunctive (active & passive)		*perfect subjunctive* (active)	*future infinitive* (active)
future participle (passive)		*pluperfect subjunctive* (active)	*perfect participle* (passive)
			future participle (active)
			perfect subjunctive (passive)
			pluperfect subjunctive (passive)

Moods of the Latin Verb

Latin verbs are classified according to mood.

The **indicative** *mood* is used to make an assertion or to ask a question.
The **subjunctive** *mood* is used to describe an action that is not real.
The **imperative** *mood* is used to make a command.

A **participle** is a verbal adjective, and an **infinitive** is a verbal noun.

Voices of the Latin Verb

Active Voice: The subject of the sentence is ***doing an action***. (A man loves a woman.)

Passive Voice: The subject of the sentence is ***receiving an action***. (A man is being loved by a woman.)

APPENDIX

Irregular Verbs

I am
(The "Being" Verb) - (sum, esse, fuī)

The Latin "being" verb is used to "link" a subject (**nominative** case) with another word in the **nominative** case that renames the subject (***predicate nominative***).

The "Being" Verb - Present Indicative

	Singular	Meaning	Plural	Meaning
1st Person	sum	I am	sumus	we are
2nd Person	es	you (s.) are	estis	you (pl.) are
3rd Person	est	he (she, it) is, there is	sunt	they are, there are

The "Being" Verb - Imperfect Indicative

	Singular	Meaning	Plural	Meaning
1st Person	eram	I was	erāmus	we were
2nd Person	erās	you (s.) were	erātis	you (pl.) were
3rd Person	erat	he (she, it) was, there was	erant	they were, there were

Notice the change in the imperfect tense vowel (ā) which is placed between the stem, er-, and the active ending.

The "Being" Verb - Future Indicative

	Singular	Meaning	Plural	Meaning
1st Person	erō	I shall be	erimus	we shall be
2nd Person	eris	you (s.) will be	eritis	you (pl.) will be
3rd Person	erit	he (she, it) will be, there will be	erunt	they will be, there will be

Notice the change in the future tense vowel (i) which is placed between the stem, er-, and the active ending.

The "Being" Verb - Infinitive

Present	Meaning	Future	Meaning
esse	to be	futūrus (-a, -um) esse	to be about to be

Irregular Verbs

I am able, I can

(possum, posse, potuī)

The irregular Latin verb possum is a compound word formed from potis (a Latin adjective meaning "able") and sum (the Latin "being" verb). Notice the variation in spelling of the combining form of potis. (When followed by the letter s, it is spelled pos-. When followed by the letter e, it is spelled pot-.)

"I am able, I can" - Present Indicative

	Singular	Meaning	Plural	Meaning
1st Person	possum	I am able	possumus	we are able
2nd Person	potes	you (s.) are able	potestis	you (pl.) are able
3rd Person	potest	he (she, it) is able	possunt	they are able

"I am able, I can" - Imperfect Indicative

	Singular	Meaning	Plural	Meaning
1st Person	poteram	I was able	poterāmus	we were able
2nd Person	poterās	you (s.) were able	poterātis	you (pl.) were able
3rd Person	poterat	he (she, it) was able	poterant	they were able

Notice the change in the imperfect tense vowel (ā) which is placed between the stem, poter-, and the active ending.

"I am able, I can" - Future Indicative

	Singular	Meaning	Plural	Meaning
1st Person	poterō	I shall be able	poterimus	we shall be able
2nd Person	poteris	you (s.) will be able	poteritis	you (pl.) will be able
3rd Person	poterit	he (she, it) will be able	poterunt	they will be able

Notice the change in the future tense vowel (i) which is placed between the stem, poter-, and the active ending.

"I am able, I can" - Infinitive

	Present	Meaning
Active	posse	to be able

APPENDIX

Irregular Verbs

I wish, I want, I am willing
(volō, velle, voluī)

In the indicative mood, the Latin verb volō is irregular in the present tense. It lacks several forms which include the future active infinitive and participle, as well as all imperative and passive forms.

"I wish, I want, I am willing" - Present Indicative

	Singular	Meaning	Plural	Meaning
1st Person	volō	I wish	volumus	we wish
2nd Person	vīs	you (s.) wish	vultis	you (pl.) wish
3rd Person	vult	he (she, it) wishes	volunt	they wish

"I wish, I want, I am willing" - Imperfect Indicative

	Singular	Meaning	Plural	Meaning
1st Person	volēbam	I was wishing	volēbāmus	we were wishing
2nd Person	volēbās	you (s.) were wishing	volēbātis	you (pl.) were wishing
3rd Person	volēbat	he (she, it) was wishing	volēbant	they were wishing

"I wish, I want, I am willing" - Future Indicative

	Singular	Meaning	Plural	Meaning
1st Person	volam	I shall wish	volēmus	we shall wish
2nd Person	volēs	you (s.) will wish	volētis	you (pl.) will wish
3rd Person	volet	he (she, it) will wish	volent	they will wish

"I wish, I want, I am willing" - Infinitive

	Present	Meaning
Active	velle	to wish

APPENDIX

Irregular Verbs

I do not wish, I am unwilling
(nōlō, nōlle, nōluī)

The Latin verb nōlō is a compound word formed from nē (a Latin conjunction meaning "not") and volō (a Latin verb meaning "I wish"). In the indicative mood, it is irregular in the present tense. It lacks several forms which include the future active infinitive and all passive forms.

"I do not wish, I am unwilling" - Present Indicative

	Singular	Meaning	Plural	Meaning
1st Person	nōlō	I do not wish	nōlumus	we do not wish
2nd Person	nōn vīs	you (s.) do not wish	nōn vultis	you (pl.) do not wish
3rd Person	nōn vult	he (she, it) does not wish	nōlunt	they do not wish

"I do not wish, I am unwilling" - Imperfect Indicative

	Singular	Meaning	Plural	Meaning
1st Person	nōlēbam	I was not wishing	nōlēbāmus	we were not wishing
2nd Person	nōlēbās	you (s.) were not wishing	nōlēbātis	you (pl.) were not wishing
3rd Person	nōlēbat	he (she, it) was not wishing	nōlēbant	they were not wishing

"I do not wish, I am unwilling" - Future Indicative

	Singular	Meaning	Plural	Meaning
1st Person	nōlam	I shall not wish	nōlēmus	we shall not wish
2nd Person	nōlēs	you (s.) will not wish	nōlētis	you (pl.) will not wish
3rd Person	nōlet	he (she, it) will not wish	nōlent	they will not wish

"I do not wish, I am unwilling" - Infinitive

	Present	Meaning
Active	nōlle	to be unwilling

APPENDIX

First Conjugation - Present Tense

A Latin verb belongs to the first conjugation if its second principal part ends in -**āre**. Its present tense stem can be found by dropping the -**re** of the second principal part. The *present tense* is used to describe an action happening in the present time.

First Conjugation - Present Active Indicative
(present indicative verb stem + active personal ending)

	Singular	Meaning	Plural	Meaning
1st Person	amō	I like (*or* I am liking) (*or* I do like)	amāmus	we like (*or* we are liking) (*or* we do like)
2nd Person	amās	you (s.) like (*or* you are liking) (*or* you do like)	amātis	you (pl.) like (*or* you are liking) (*or* you do like)
3rd Person	amat	he (she, it) likes (*or* he is liking) (*or* he does like)	amant	they like (*or* they are liking) (*or* they do like)

First Conjugation - Present Passive Indicative
(present indicative verb stem + passive personal ending)

	Singular	Meaning	Plural	Meaning
1st Person	amor	I am liked (*or* I am being liked)	amāmur	we are liked (*or* we are being liked)
2nd Person	amāris	you (s.) are liked (*or* you are being liked)	amāminī	you (pl.) are liked (*or* you are being liked)
3rd Person	amātur	he (she, it) is liked (*or* he is being liked)	amantur	they are liked (*or* they are being liked)

First Conjugation - Present Infinitive

	Present	Meaning
Active	amāre	to like
Passive	amārī	to be liked

APPENDIX

First Conjugation - Imperfect Tense

A Latin verb belongs to the first conjugation if its second principal part ends in -āre. Its present tense stem can be found by dropping the -re of the second principal part. The *imperfect tense* is used to describe a continuous action in past time.

First Conjugation - Imperfect Active Indicative
(present indicative verb stem + imperfect tense indicator [-bā-] + active personal ending)

	Singular	Meaning	Plural	Meaning
1st Person	amābam	I was liking (*or* I used to like)	amābāmus	we were liking (*or* we used to like)
2nd Person	amābās	you (s.) were liking (*or* you used to like)	amābātis	you (pl.) were liking (*or* you used to like)
3rd Person	amābat	he (she, it) was liking (*or* he used to like)	amābant	they were liking (*or* they used to like)

First Conjugation - Imperfect Passive Indicative
(present indicative verb stem + imperfect tense indicator [-bā-] + passive personal ending)

	Singular	Meaning	Plural	Meaning
1st Person	amābar	I was being liked (*or* I used to be liked)	amābāmur	we were being liked (*or* we used to be liked)
2nd Person	amābāris	you (s.) were being liked (*or* you used to be liked)	amābāminī	you (pl.) were being liked (*or* you used to be liked)
3rd Person	amābātur	he (she, it) was being liked (*or* he used to be liked)	amābantur	they were being liked (*or* they used to be liked)

APPENDIX

First Conjugation - Future Tense

A Latin verb belongs to the first conjugation if its second principal part ends in -āre. Its present tense stem can be found by dropping the -re of the second principal part. The *future tense* is used to describe an action that will take place in the future.

First Conjugation - Future Active Indicative
(present indicative verb stem + future tense indicator [-bi-] + active personal ending)

	Singular	Meaning	Plural	Meaning
1st Person	amābō	I shall like	amābimus	we shall like
2nd Person	amābis	you (s.) will like	amābitis	you (pl.) will like
3rd Person	amābit	he (she, it) will like	amābunt	they will like

The vowel (i) of the future tense indicator (bi) changes to ō in the first person singular and to u in the third person plural.

First Conjugation - Future Passive Indicative
(present indicative verb stem + future tense indicator [-bi-] + passive personal ending)

	Singular	Meaning	Plural	Meaning
1st Person	amābor	I shall be liked	amābimur	we shall be liked
2nd Person	amāberis	you (s.) will be liked	amābiminī	you (pl.) will be liked
3rd Person	amābitur	he (she, it) will be liked	amābuntur	they will be liked

---

First Conjugation - Future Infinitive*

	Future	Meaning
Active	amātūrus (-a, -um) esse	to be about to like

*Future passive infinitives are rare and are therefore not included in this workbook.

APPENDIX

Second Conjugation - Present Tense

A Latin verb belongs to the second conjugation if its second principal part ends in -ēre. Its present tense stem can be found by dropping the -re of the second principal part. The **present tense** is used to describe an action happening in the present time.

Second Conjugation - Present Active Indicative
(present indicative verb stem + active personal ending)

	Singular	Meaning	Plural	Meaning
1st Person	moneō	I warn (*or* I am warning) (*or* I do warn)	monēmus	we warn (*or* we are warning) (*or* we do warn)
2nd Person	monēs	you (s.) warn (*or* you are warning) (*or* you do warn)	monētis	you (pl.) warn (*or* you are warning) (*or* you do warn)
3rd Person	monet	he (she, it) warns (*or* he is warning) (*or* he does warn)	monent	they warn (*or* they are warning) (*or* they do warn)

Second Conjugation - Present Passive Indicative
(present indicative verb stem + passive personal ending)

	Singular	Meaning	Plural	Meaning
1st Person	moneor	I am warned (*or* I am being warned)	monēmur	we are warned (*or* we are being warned)
2nd Person	monēris	you (s.) are warned (*or* you are being warned)	monēminī	you (pl.) are warned (*or* you are being warned)
3rd Person	monētur	he (she, it) is warned (*or* he is being warned)	monentur	they are warned (*or* they are being warned)

Second Conjugation - Present Infinitive

	Present	Meaning
Active	monēre	to warn
Passive	monērī	to be warned

APPENDIX

Second Conjugation - Imperfect Tense

A Latin verb belongs to the second conjugation if its second principal part ends in -ēre. Its present tense stem can be found by dropping the -re of the second principal part. The *imperfect tense* is used to describe a continuous action in past time.

Second Conjugation - Imperfect Active Indicative
(present indicative verb stem + imperfect tense indicator [-bā-] + active personal ending)

	Singular	Meaning	Plural	Meaning
1st Person	monēbam	I was warning (*or* I used to warn)	monēbāmus	we were warning (*or* we used to warn)
2nd Person	monēbās	you (s.) were warning (*or* you used to warn)	monēbātis	you (pl.) were warning (*or* you used to warn)
3rd Person	monēbat	he (she, it) was warning (*or* he used to warn)	monēbant	they were warning (*or* they used to warn)

Second Conjugation - Imperfect Passive Indicative
(present indicative verb stem + imperfect tense indicator [-bā-] + passive personal ending)

	Singular	Meaning	Plural	Meaning
1st Person	monēbar	I was being warned (*or* I used to be warned)	monēbāmur	we were being warned (*or* we used to be warned)
2nd Person	monēbāris	you (s.) were being warned (*or* you used to be warned)	monēbāminī	you (pl.) were being warned (*or* you used to be warned)
3rd Person	monēbātur	he (she, it) was being warned (*or* he used to be warned)	monēbantur	they were being warned (*or* they used to be warned)

APPENDIX

Second Conjugation - Future Tense

A Latin verb belongs to the second conjugation if its second principal part ends in -ēre. Its present tense stem can be found by dropping the -re of the second principal part. The *future tense* is used to describe an action that will take place in the future.

Second Conjugation - Future Active Indicative
(present indicative verb stem + future tense indicator [-bi-] + active personal ending)

	Singular	Meaning	Plural	Meaning
1st Person	monēbō	I shall warn	monēbimus	we shall warn
2nd Person	monēbis	you (s.) will warn	monēbitis	you (pl.) will warn
3rd Person	monēbit	he (she, it) will warn	monēbunt	they will warn

The vowel (i) of the future tense indicator (bi) changes to ō in the first person singular and to u in the third person plural.

Second Conjugation - Future Passive Indicative
(present indicative verb stem + future tense indicator [-bi-] + passive personal ending)

	Singular	Meaning	Plural	Meaning
1st Person	monēbor	I shall be warned	monēbimur	we shall be warned
2nd Person	monēberis	you (s.) will be warned	monēbiminī	you (pl.) will be warned
3rd Person	monēbitur	he (she, it) will be warned	monēbuntur	they will be warned

*Second Conjugation - Future Infinitive**

	Future	Meaning
Active	monitūrus (-a, -um) esse	to be about to warn

*Future passive infinitives are rare and are therefore not included in this workbook.

Third Conjugation - Present Tense

A Latin verb belongs to the third conjugation if its second principal part ends in -ere. Its present tense stem can be found by dropping the -ō of the first principal part. The *present tense* is used to describe an action happening in the present time.

Third Conjugation - Present Active Indicative
(present indicative verb stem + active personal ending)

	Singular	Meaning	Plural	Meaning
1st Person	dīcō	I tell (*or* I am telling) (*or* I do tell)	dīcimus	we tell (*or* we are telling) (*or* we do tell)
2nd Person	dīcis	you (s.) tell (*or* you are telling) (*or* you do tell)	dīcitis	you (pl.) tell (*or* you are telling) (*or* you do tell)
3rd Person	dīcit	he (she, it) tells (*or* he is telling) (*or* he does tell)	dīcunt	they tell (*or* they are telling) (*or* they do tell)

Third Conjugation - Present Passive Indicative
(present indicative verb stem + passive personal ending)

	Singular	Meaning	Plural	Meaning
1st Person	dīcor	I am told (*or* I am being told)	dīcimur	we are told (*or* we are being told)
2nd Person	dīceris	you (s.) are told (*or* you are being told)	dīciminī	you (pl.) are told (*or* you are being told)
3rd Person	dīcitur	he (she, it) is told (*or* he is being told)	dīcuntur	they are told (*or* they are being told)

Third Conjugation - Present Infinitive

	Present	Meaning
Active	dīcere	to tell
Passive	dīcī	to be told

APPENDIX

Third Conjugation - Imperfect Tense

A Latin verb belongs to the third conjugation if its second principal part ends in -ere. Its present tense stem can be found by dropping the -ō of the first principal part. The *imperfect tense* is used to describe a continuous action in past time.

Third Conjugation - Imperfect Active Indicative
(present indicative verb stem + imperfect tense indicator [-ēbā-] + active personal ending)

	Singular	Meaning	Plural	Meaning
1st Person	dīcēbam	I was telling (*or* I used to tell)	dīcēbāmus	we were telling (*or* we used to tell)
2nd Person	dīcēbās	you (s.) were telling (*or* you used to tell)	dīcēbātis	you (pl.) were telling (*or* you used to tell)
3rd Person	dīcēbat	he (she, it) was telling (*or* he used to tell)	dīcēbant	they were telling (*or* they used to tell)

Third Conjugation - Imperfect Passive Indicative
(present indicative verb stem + imperfect tense indicator [-ēbā-] + passive personal ending)

	Singular	Meaning	Plural	Meaning
1st Person	dīcēbar	I was being told (*or* I used to be told)	dīcēbāmur	we were being told (*or* we used to be told)
2nd Person	dīcēbāris	you (s.) were being told (*or* you used to be told)	dīcēbāminī	you (pl.) were being told (*or* you used to be told)
3rd Person	dīcēbātur	he (she, it) was being told (*or* he used to be told)	dīcēbantur	they were being told (*or* they used to be told)

APPENDIX

Third Conjugation - Future Tense

A Latin verb belongs to the third conjugation if its second principal part ends in -ere. Its present tense stem can be found by dropping the -ō of the first principal part. The *future tense* is used to describe an action that will take place in the future.

Third Conjugation - Future Active Indicative
(present indicative verb stem + future tense indicator [-ē-] + active personal ending)

	Singular	Meaning	Plural	Meaning
1st Person	dīcam	I shall tell	dīcēmus	we shall tell
2nd Person	dīcēs	you (s.) will tell	dīcētis	you (pl.) will tell
3rd Person	dīcet	he (she, it) will tell	dīcent	they will tell

The future tense indicator (ē) becomes short (e) before -t and -nt. The ē changes to a in the first person singular.

Third Conjugation - Future Passive Indicative
(present indicative verb stem + future tense indicator [-ē-] + passive personal ending)

	Singular	Meaning	Plural	Meaning
1st Person	dīcar	I shall be told	dīcēmur	we shall be told
2nd Person	dīcēris	you (s.) will be told	dīcēminī	you (pl.) will be told
3rd Person	dīcētur	he (she, it) will be told	dīcentur	they will be told

*Third Conjugation - Future Infinitive**

	Future	Meaning
Active	dīctūrus (-a, -um) esse	to be about to tell

*Future passive infinitives are rare and are therefore not included in this workbook.

Latin Workbook - Level 6
Copyright © 2006 by Karen Mohs

APPENDIX

Third I-Stem Conjugation - Present Tense

A Latin verb belongs to the third i-stem conjugation if its second principal part ends in -ere and its present tense stem ends in -i. Its present tense stem can be found by dropping the -ō of the first principal part. The **present tense** is used to describe an action happening in the present time.

Third I-Stem Conjugation - Present Active Indicative
(present indicative verb stem + active personal ending)

	Singular	Meaning	Plural	Meaning
1st Person	capiō	I take (*or* I am taking) (*or* I do take)	capimus	we take (*or* we are taking) (*or* we do take)
2nd Person	capis	you (s.) take (*or* you are taking) (*or* you do take)	capitis	you (pl.) take (*or* you are taking) (*or* you do take)
3rd Person	capit	he (she, it) takes (*or* he is taking) (*or* he does take)	capiunt	they take (*or* they are taking) (*or* they do take)

Third I-Stem Conjugation - Present Passive Indicative
(present indicative verb stem + passive personal ending)

	Singular	Meaning	Plural	Meaning
1st Person	capior	I am taken (*or* I am being taken)	capimur	we are taken (*or* we are being taken)
2nd Person	caperis	you (s.) are taken (*or* you are being taken)	capiminī	you (pl.) are taken (*or* you are being taken)
3rd Person	capitur	he (she, it) is taken (*or* he is being taken)	capiuntur	they are taken (*or* they are being taken)

Third I-Stem Conjugation - Present Infinitive

	Present	Meaning
Active	capere	to take
Passive	capī	to be taken

APPENDIX

Third I-Stem Conjugation - Imperfect Tense

A Latin verb belongs to the third i-stem conjugation if its second principal part ends in -ere and its present tense stem ends in -i. Its present tense stem can be found by dropping the -ō of the first principal part. The *imperfect tense* is used to describe a continuous action in past time.

Third I-Stem Conjugation - Imperfect Active Indicative
(present indicative verb stem + imperfect tense indicator [-ēbā-] + active personal ending)

	Singular	Meaning	Plural	Meaning
1st Person	capiēbam	I was taking (*or* I used to take)	capiēbāmus	we were taking (*or* we used to take)
2nd Person	capiēbās	you (s.) were taking (*or* you used to take)	capiēbātis	you (pl.) were taking (*or* you used to take)
3rd Person	capiēbat	he (she, it) was taking (*or* he used to take)	capiēbant	they were taking (*or* they used to take)

Third I-Stem Conjugation - Imperfect Passive Indicative
(present indicative verb stem + imperfect tense indicator [-ēbā-] + passive personal ending)

	Singular	Meaning	Plural	Meaning
1st Person	capiēbar	I was being taken (*or* I used to be taken)	capiēbāmur	we were being taken (*or* we used to be taken)
2nd Person	capiēbāris	you (s.) were being taken (*or* you used to be taken)	capiēbāminī	you (pl.) were being taken (*or* you used to be taken)
3rd Person	capiēbātur	he (she, it) was being taken (*or* he used to be taken)	capiēbantur	they were being taken (*or* they used to be taken)

APPENDIX

Third I-Stem Conjugation - Future Tense

A Latin verb belongs to the third i-stem conjugation if its second principal part ends in -ere and its present tense stem ends in -i. Its present tense stem can be found by dropping the -ō of the first principal part. The *future tense* is used to describe an action that will take place in the future.

Third I-Stem Conjugation - Future Active Indicative
(present indicative verb stem + future tense indicator [-ē-] + active personal ending)

	Singular	Meaning	Plural	Meaning
1st Person	capiam	I shall take	capiēmus	we shall take
2nd Person	capiēs	you (s.) will take	capiētis	you (pl.) will take
3rd Person	capiet	he (she, it) will take	capient	they will take

The future tense indicator (ē) becomes short (e) before -t and -nt. The ē changes to a in the first person singular.

Third I-Stem Conjugation - Future Passive Indicative
(present indicative verb stem + future tense indicator [-ē-] + passive personal ending)

	Singular	Meaning	Plural	Meaning
1st Person	capiar	I shall be taken	capiēmur	we shall be taken
2nd Person	capiēris	you (s.) will be taken	capiēminī	you (pl.) will be taken
3rd Person	capiētur	he (she, it) will be taken	capientur	they will be taken

Third I-Stem Conjugation - Future Infinitive*

	Future	Meaning
Active	captūrus (-a, -um) esse	to be about to take

*Future passive infinitives are rare and are therefore not included in this workbook.

APPENDIX

Fourth Conjugation - Present Tense

A Latin verb belongs to the fourth conjugation if its second principal part ends in -īre. Its present tense stem can be found by dropping the -re of the second principal part. The *present tense* is used to describe an action happening in the present time.

Fourth Conjugation - Present Active Indicative
(present indicative verb stem + active personal ending)

	Singular	Meaning	Plural	Meaning
1st Person	audiō	I hear (*or* I am hearing) (*or* I do hear)	audīmus	we hear (*or* we are hearing) (*or* we do hear)
2nd Person	audīs	you (s.) hear (*or* you are hearing) (*or* you do hear)	audītis	you (pl.) hear (*or* you are hearing) (*or* you do hear)
3rd Person	audit	he (she, it) hears (*or* he is hearing) (*or* he does hear)	audiunt	they hear (*or* they are hearing) (*or* they do hear)

Fourth Conjugation - Present Passive Indicative
(present indicative verb stem + passive personal ending)

	Singular	Meaning	Plural	Meaning
1st Person	audior	I am heard (*or* I am being heard)	audīmur	we are heard (*or* we are being heard)
2nd Person	audīris	you (s.) are heard (*or* you are being heard)	audīminī	you (pl.) are heard (*or* you are being heard)
3rd Person	audītur	he (she, it) is heard (*or* he is being heard)	audiuntur	they are heard (*or* they are being heard)

Fourth Conjugation - Present Infinitive

	Present	Meaning
Active	audīre	to hear
Passive	audīrī	to be heard

APPENDIX

Fourth Conjugation - Imperfect Tense

A Latin verb belongs to the fourth conjugation if its second principal part ends in -īre. Its present tense stem can be found by dropping the -re of the second principal part. The ***imperfect tense*** is used to describe a continuous action in past time.

Fourth Conjugation - Imperfect Active Indicative
(present indicative verb stem + imperfect tense indicator [-ēbā-] + active personal ending)

	Singular	Meaning	Plural	Meaning
1st Person	audiēbam	I was hearing (*or* I used to hear)	audiēbāmus	we were hearing (*or* we used to hear)
2nd Person	audiēbās	you (s.) were hearing (*or* you used to hear)	audiēbātis	you (pl.) were hearing (*or* you used to hear)
3rd Person	audiēbat	he (she, it) was hearing (*or* he used to hear)	audiēbant	they were hearing (*or* they used to hear)

Fourth Conjugation - Imperfect Passive Indicative
(present indicative verb stem + imperfect tense indicator [-ēbā-] + passive personal ending)

	Singular	Meaning	Plural	Meaning
1st Person	audiēbar	I was being heard (*or* I used to be heard)	audiēbāmur	we were being heard (*or* we used to be heard)
2nd Person	audiēbāris	you (s.) were being heard (*or* you used to be heard)	audiēbāminī	you (pl.) were being heard (*or* you used to be heard)
3rd Person	audiēbātur	he (she, it) was being heard (*or* he used to be heard)	audiēbantur	they were being heard (*or* they used to be heard)

APPENDIX

Fourth Conjugation - Future Tense

A Latin verb belongs to the fourth conjugation if its second principal part ends in -īre. Its present tense stem can be found by dropping the -re of the second principal part. The *future tense* is used to describe an action that will take place in the future.

Fourth Conjugation - Future Active Indicative
(present indicative verb stem + future tense indicator [-ē-] + active personal ending)

	Singular	Meaning	Plural	Meaning
1st Person	audiam	I shall hear	audiēmus	we shall hear
2nd Person	audiēs	you (s.) will hear	audiētis	you (pl.) will hear
3rd Person	audiet	he (she, it) will hear	audient	they will hear

The future tense indicator (ē) becomes short (e) before -t and -nt. The ē changes to a in the first person singular.

Fourth Conjugation - Future Passive Indicative
(present indicative verb stem + future tense indicator [-ē-] + passive personal ending)

	Singular	Meaning	Plural	Meaning
1st Person	audiar	I shall be heard	audiēmur	we shall be heard
2nd Person	audiēris	you (s.) will be heard	audiēminī	you (pl.) will be heard
3rd Person	audiētur	he (she, it) will be heard	audientur	they will be heard

*Fourth Conjugation - Future Infinitive**

	Future	Meaning
Active	audītūrus (-a, -um) esse	to be about to hear

*Future passive infinitives are rare and are therefore not included in this workbook.

Infinitives

An infinitive is a verbal noun. Therefore, it can act in some ways like a *noun* (it can function as a subject or as an object), but it is also like a *verb* (it has tense and voice).

The three tenses of Latin infinitives: present, future, and perfect.

The *present* infinitive is the second principal part of the Latin verb. (See page 15.)

APPENDIX

Uses of Infinitives

Subjective Infinitive

An infinitive acting as a subject:

- Vidēre est scīre. - **To see** is to know.

Complementary Infinitive

An infinitive acting as an object - required by certain verbs to complete their meaning:

- Cupit edere. - He wants **to eat**.

Verbs such as parō, cupiō, cōnstituō, temptō, dēbeō, possum, and prohibeō may require an infinitive to complete their meaning.

Objective Infinitive

An infinitive acting as an object with its subject in the accusative case:

- Iubet virōs edere. - He orders **the men to eat**.

Verbs such as iubeō, cōgō, and prohibeō are commonly used with the objective infinitive.

Indirect Statement

An infinitive with a subject in the accusative case used to report something indirectly (used after verbs of saying, thinking, knowing, and perceiving):

Statement: Puer edit. - The boy eats.

Indirectly Reported: Vir dīcit puerum edere. - The man says that the boy eats.

Saying verbs include dīcō, nūntiō, nārrō, scrībō, doceō, dēmōnstrō, moneō, etc.
Knowing verbs include sciō, memoriā teneō, etc.
Thinking verbs include cernō, cōgitō, crēdō, habeō, putō, spērō, etc.
Perceiving and *feeling* verbs include audiō, videō, etc.

APPENDIX

Word Order

Word order in Latin is not the same as word order in English. In Latin, since the ending determines the role the word plays in the sentence, word order is generally used for emphasis. However, there is a tendency to put the verb last.

Gender and Case of the Latin Noun

The three genders of Latin nouns are masculine, feminine, and neuter.

Latin nouns are declined using five main *cases*.

The subject of the sentence as well as a noun "linked" to the subject with a linking verb (e.g. *is* or *are*) belong in the **nominative** case. Possession is expressed with the **genitive** case. The indirect object belongs in the **dative** case. The direct object belongs in the **accusative** case. The **ablative** case is used to express special relationships. These cases have other important uses as well.

Special Case Uses

Ablative Case

Ablative of Accompaniment
   To indicate accompaniment, use the preposition cum with the ablative case.

Ablative of Description
   To describe the character, size, or quality of a noun which has a modifying adjective, use a second noun in the ablative case. In descriptions of *physical traits*, the *ablative of description* is used.

Ablative of Manner
   To indicate the manner in which an action is performed, use the preposition cum with the ablative case. If an adjective is used, cum may be omitted. If cum is used, it is placed between the adjective and the noun.

Ablative of Means or Instrument
   To indicate the means or instrument by which something is done, use the ablative case without a preposition.

Ablative of Personal Agent
   To indicate the *person* performing an action when the verb is *passive*, use the preposition ā/ab with the ablative case.

APPENDIX

Special Case Uses (continued)

Ablative Case (continued)

Ablative of Place From Which

To indicate location *from which* motion takes place, use the prepositions ā/ab, dē, or ē/ex with the ablative case.

Ablative of Place Where

To indicate location "in" or "on," use the preposition in with the ablative case.
To indicate location "under," use the preposition sub with the ablative case.

Ablative of Separation

To indicate *separation* when there is *no* active movement, use the ablative case with or without the preposition ā/ab. For concrete nouns, the ablative case is generally used with the preposition. For abstract nouns, the ablative case is generally used without the preposition.

Ablative of Time When

To indicate the *time when* an action occurs, use the ablative case without a preposition.

Ablative of Time Within Which

To indicate the *time within which* an action occurs, use the ablative case without a preposition.

Accusative Case

Accusative of Place to Which

To indicate location "into," use the preposition in with the accusative case.
To indicate location "to," use the preposition ad with the accusative case.
To indicate location "up to," use the preposition sub with the accusative case.

Genitive Case

Genitive of Description (Genitive of Measure)

To describe the character, size, or quality of a noun which has a modifying adjective, use a second noun in the genitive case. When describing *definite measurement*, the *genitive of description* is often called the *genitive of measure*.

Objective Genitive

To indicate the *object* of a noun when that noun implies *feeling* or *action*, use a second noun in the genitive case. This *objective genitive* case, which connects two nouns, can be translated with words such as *for*, *of*, *from*, etc.

Partitive Genitive (Genitive of the Whole)

To indicate the *whole* of which something is a part, use a noun in the genitive case. This noun in the genitive case follows the noun, pronoun, or adjective which designates the *part* of the whole. (To indicate the *partitive* idea with certain words such as cardinal numbers, use dē or ex with the *ablative of place from which* instead of the *partitive genitive*.)

APPENDIX

First Declension

A Latin noun belongs to the first declension if the genitive singular ends in -ae. Remove the -ae from the genitive singular to find the stem. These nouns are usually feminine, unless they describe males in Latin culture such as sailors, poets, or farmers.

	Singular	*Meaning*	*Plural*	*Meaning*
Nominative	puella	a girl (*or* the girl)	puellae	girls (*or* the girls)
Genitive	puellae	of a girl (*or* of the girl)	puellārum	of girls (*or* of the girls)
Dative	puellae	to/for a girl (*or* to/for the girl)	puellīs	to/for girls (*or* to/for the girls)
Accusative	puellam	a girl (*or* the girl)	puellās	girls (*or* the girls)
Abative	puellā	by/with* a girl (*or* by/with* the girl)	puellīs	by/with* girls (*or* by/with* the girls)

*The translations given above are just a sampling of the many possible meanings of the ablative case.

Second Declension

A Latin noun belongs to the second declension if the genitive singular ends in -ī. Remove the -ī from the genitive singular to find the stem. If a second declension nominative ends in -us, it is usually masculine.

	Singular	*Meaning*	*Plural*	*Meaning*
Nominative	amīcus	a friend (*or* the friend)	amīcī	friends (*or* the friends)
Genitive	amīcī	of a friend (*or* of the friend)	amīcōrum	of friends (*or* of the friends)
Dative	amīcō	to/for a friend (*or* to/for the friend)	amīcīs	to/for friends (*or* to/for the friends)
Accusative	amīcum	a friend (*or* the friend)	amīcōs	friends (*or* the friends)
Abative	amīcō	by/with* a friend (*or* by/with* the friend)	amīcīs	by/with* friends (*or* by/with* the friends)

*The translations given above are just a sampling of the many possible meanings of the ablative case.

APPENDIX

Second Declension -ius

A Latin second declension -ius noun is declined like a second declension -us noun except in the genitive singular. The expected genitive singular -iī of these -ius nouns is shortened to -ī. However, the stem retains the -i- [soci-].

	Singular	Meaning	Plural	Meaning
Nominative	socius	an ally (*or* the ally)	sociī	allies (*or* the allies)
Genitive	socī	of an ally (*or* of the ally)	sociōrum	of allies (*or* of the allies)
Dative	sociō	to/for an ally (*or* to/for the ally)	sociīs	to/for allies (*or* to/for the allies)
Accusative	socium	an ally (*or* the ally)	sociōs	allies (*or* the allies)
Abative	sociō	by/with* an ally (*or* by/with* the ally)	sociīs	by/with* allies (*or* by/with* the allies)

*The translations given above are just a sampling of the many possible meanings of the ablative case.

Second Declension -er
(as in puer)

A Latin noun belongs to the second declension if the genitive singular ends in -ī. Remove the -ī from the genitive singular to find the stem. If a second declension nominative ends in -er, it is usually masculine.

	Singular	Meaning	Plural	Meaning
Nominative	puer	a boy (*or* the boy)	puerī	boys (*or* the boys)
Genitive	puerī	of a boy (*or* of the boy)	puerōrum	of boys (*or* of the boys)
Dative	puerō	to/for a boy (*or* to/for the boy)	puerīs	to/for boys (*or* to/for the boys)
Accusative	puerum	a boy (*or* the boy)	puerōs	boys (*or* the boys)
Abative	puerō	by/with* a boy (*or* by/with* the boy)	puerīs	by/with* boys (*or* by/with* the boys)

*The translations given above are just a sampling of the many possible meanings of the ablative case.

APPENDIX

Second Declension -er
(as in ager)

A Latin noun belongs to the second declension if the genitive singular ends in -ī. Remove the -ī from the genitive singular to find the stem. If a second declension nominative ends in -er, it is usually masculine.

	Singular	*Meaning*	*Plural*	*Meaning*
Nominative	ager	a field (*or* the field)	agrī	fields (*or* the fields)
Genitive	agrī	of a field (*or* of the field)	agrōrum	of fields (*or* of the fields)
Dative	agrō	to/for a field (*or* to/for the field)	agrīs	to/for fields (*or* to/for the fields)
Accusative	agrum	a field (*or* the field)	agrōs	fields (*or* the fields)
Abative	agrō	by/with* a field (*or* by/with* the field)	agrīs	by/with* fields (*or* by/with* the fields)

*The translations given above are just a sampling of the many possible meanings of the ablative case.

Second Declension Neuter

A Latin noun belongs to the second declension if the genitive singular ends in -ī. Remove the -ī from the genitive singular to find the stem. If a second declension nominative ends in -um, it is neuter.

	Singular	*Meaning*	*Plural*	*Meaning*
Nominative	caelum	a sky (*or* the sky)	caela	skies (*or* the skies)
Genitive	caelī	of a sky (*or* of the sky)	caelōrum	of skies (*or* of the skies)
Dative	caelō	to/for a sky (*or* to/for the sky)	caelīs	to/for skies (*or* to/for the skies)
Accusative	caelum	a sky (*or* the sky)	caela	skies (*or* the skies)
Abative	caelō	by/with* a sky (*or* by/with* the sky)	caelīs	by/with* skies (*or* by/with* the skies)

*The translations given above are just a sampling of the many possible meanings of the ablative case.

APPENDIX

Third Declension
(as in frāter)

A Latin noun belongs to the third declension if the genitive singular ends in -is. Remove the -is from the genitive singular to find the stem.

	Singular	Meaning	Plural	Meaning
Nominative	frāter	a brother (*or* the brother)	frātrēs	brothers (*or* the brothers)
Genitive	frātris	of a brother (*or* of the brother)	frātrum	of brothers (*or* of the brothers)
Dative	frātrī	to/for a brother (*or* to/for the brother)	frātribus	to/for brothers (*or* to/for the brothers)
Accusative	frātrem	a brother (*or* the brother)	frātrēs	brothers (*or* the brothers)
Abative	frātre	by/with* a brother (*or* by/with* the brother)	frātribus	by/with* brothers (*or* by/with* the brothers)

*The translations given above are just a sampling of the many possible meanings of the ablative case.

Third Declension
(as in soror)

A Latin noun belongs to the third declension if the genitive singular ends in -is. Remove the -is from the genitive singular to find the stem.

	Singular	Meaning	Plural	Meaning
Nominative	soror	a sister (*or* the sister)	sorōrēs	sisters (*or* the sisters)
Genitive	sorōris	of a sister (*or* of the sister)	sorōrum	of sisters (*or* of the sisters)
Dative	sorōrī	to/for a sister (*or* to/for the sister)	sorōribus	to/for sisters (*or* to/for the sisters)
Accusative	sorōrem	a sister (*or* the sister)	sorōrēs	sisters (*or* the sisters)
Abative	sorōre	by/with* a sister (*or* by/with* the sister)	sorōribus	by/with* sisters (*or* by/with* the sisters)

*The translations given above are just a sampling of the many possible meanings of the ablative case.

APPENDIX

Third Declension I-Stem

A Latin noun belongs to the third declension if the genitive singular ends in -is. Remove the -is from the genitive singular to find the stem. Certain third declension nouns require an -ium (rather than -um) ending in the genitive plural. These "third declension i-stems" include the following:

1. a masculine or feminine noun that ends in -ēs or -is in the nominative singular and has the same number of syllables in the **nominative** and **genitive** singular cases (e.g. hostis)
2. a masculine or feminine noun that ends in -ns or -rs (e.g. gēns)
3. a masculine or feminine noun that has only one syllable in the nominative singular and its stem ends in two consonants (e.g. urbs)
4. a neuter noun that ends in -al or -e in the nominative singular (e.g. mare)

Notice the -ī in the ablative singular and the -ia in the nominative and accusative plural of **neuter** third declension i-stems.

Singular

Nominative	hostis	gēns	urbs	mare
Genitive	hostis	gentis	urbis	maris
Dative	hostī	gentī	urbī	marī
Accusative	hostem	gentem	urbem	mare
Abative	hoste	gente	urbe	marī

Plural

Nominative	hostēs	gentēs	urbēs	maria
Genitive	hostium	gentium	urbium	marium
Dative	hostibus	gentibus	urbibus	maribus
Accusative	hostēs	gentēs	urbēs	maria
Abative	hostibus	gentibus	urbibus	maribus

APPENDIX

Third Declension Neuter

A Latin noun belongs to the third declension if the genitive singular ends in -is. Remove the -is from the genitive singular to find the stem. Neuter nouns have the same ending in the nominative and accusative cases. Plural nominative and accusative neuter nouns always end in -a.

	Singular	Meaning	Plural	Meaning
Nominative	nōmen	a name (*or* the name)	nōmina	names (*or* the names)
Genitive	nōminis	of a name (*or* of the name)	nōminum	of names (*or* of the names)
Dative	nōminī	to/for a name (*or* to/for the name)	nōminibus	to/for names (*or* to/for the names)
Accusative	nōmen	a name (*or* the name)	nōmina	names (*or* the names)
Abative	nōmine	by/with* a name (*or* by/with* the name)	nōminibus	by/with* names (*or* by/with* the names)

*The translations given above are just a sampling of the many possible meanings of the ablative case.

Fourth Declension

A Latin noun belongs to the fourth declension if the genitive singular ends in -ūs. Remove the -ūs from the genitive singular to find the stem. These nouns are usually masculine. However, manus is feminine.

	Singular	Meaning	Plural	Meaning
Nominative	manus	a hand (*or* the hand)	manūs	hands (*or* the hands)
Genitive	manūs	of a hand (*or* of the hand)	manuum	of hands (*or* of the hands)
Dative	manuī	to/for a hand (*or* to/for the hand)	manibus	to/for hands (*or* to/for the hands)
Accusative	manum	a hand (*or* the hand)	manūs	hands (*or* the hands)
Abative	manū	by/with* a hand (*or* by/with* the hand)	manibus	by/with* hands (*or* by/with* the hands)

*The translations given above are just a sampling of the many possible meanings of the ablative case.

APPENDIX

Fourth Declension Neuter

A Latin noun belongs to the fourth declension if the genitive singular ends in -ūs. Remove the -ūs from the genitive singular to find the stem. If a fourth declension nominative ends in ū, it is neuter. Neuter nouns have the same ending in the nominative and accusative cases. Plural nominative and accusative neuter nouns always end in -a.

	Singular	Meaning	Plural	Meaning
Nominative	cornū	a horn (*or* the horn)	cornua	horns (*or* the horns)
Genitive	cornūs	of a horn (*or* of the horn)	cornuum	of horns (*or* of the horns)
Dative	cornū	to/for a horn (*or* to/for the horn)	cornibus	to/for horns (*or* to/for the horns)
Accusative	cornū	a horn (*or* the horn)	cornua	horns (*or* the horns)
Abative	cornū	by/with* a horn (*or* by/with* the horn)	cornibus	by/with* horns (*or* by/with* the horns)

*The translations given above are just a sampling of the many possible meanings of the ablative case.

APPENDIX

Fifth Declension
(as in diēs)

A Latin noun belongs to the fifth declension if the genitive singular ends in -ēī or -eī. Remove the ending from the genitive singular to find the stem. (The fifth declension ending is actually -ī. The -ē- [or -e- if after a consonant and before a vowel] is the stem ending. However, it is easy to recognize this declension by the -ēī or -eī of the genitive singular.)

	Singular	*Meaning*	*Plural*	*Meaning*
Nominative	diēs	a day (*or* the day)	diēs	days (*or* the days)
Genitive	diēī	of a day (*or* of the day)	diērum	of days (*or* of the days)
Dative	diēī	to/for a day (*or* to/for the day)	diēbus	to/for days (*or* to/for the days)
Accusative	diem	a day (*or* the day)	diēs	days (*or* the days)
Abative	diē	by/with* a day (*or* by/with* the day)	diēbus	by/with* days (*or* by/with* the days)

*The translations given above are just a sampling of the many possible meanings of the ablative case.

Fifth Declension
(as in spēs)

	Singular	*Meaning*	*Plural*	*Meaning*
Nominative	spēs	a hope (*or* the hope)	spēs	hopes (*or* the hopes)
Genitive	speī	of a hope (*or* of the hope)	spērum	of hopes (*or* of the hopes)
Dative	speī	to/for a hope (*or* to/for the hope)	spēbus	to/for hopes (*or* to/for the hopes)
Accusative	spem	a hope (*or* the hope)	spēs	hopes (*or* the hopes)
Abative	spē	by/with* a hope (*or* by/with* the hope)	spēbus	by/with* hopes (*or* by/with* the hopes)

*The translations given above are just a sampling of the many possible meanings of the ablative case.

APPENDIX

Adjectives

Adjectives in Latin, as in English, are words that modify nouns or pronouns. Latin adjectives agree with the words they modify in gender, number, and case. Therefore each adjective has three genders (masculine, feminine, neuter), two numbers (singular, plural), and five cases (nominative, genitive, dative, accusative, ablative).

First and Second Declension Adjectives

Latin adjectives ending in -us, -a, -um are first and second declension adjectives. They have second declension forms in the masculine and neuter and first declension forms in the feminine.

	Singular			*Plural*		
	Masculine	Feminine	Neuter	Masculine	Feminine	Neuter
Nominative	bonus	bona	bonum	bonī	bonae	bona
Genitive	bonī	bonae	bonī	bonōrum	bonārum	bonōrum
Dative	bonō	bonae	bonō	bonīs	bonīs	bonīs
Accusative	bonum	bonam	bonum	bonōs	bonās	bona
Ablative	bonō	bonā	bonō	bonīs	bonīs	bonīs

First and Second Declension Adjectives - er forms

Some Latin first and second declension adjectives end in -er. Of these adjectives ending in -er, some retain the vowel in the stem (as in miser), but most do not (as in pulcher).

	Singular			*Plural*		
	Masculine	Feminine	Neuter	Masculine	Feminine	Neuter
Nominative	miser	misera	miserum	miserī	miserae	misera
Genitive	miserī	miserae	miserī	miserōrum	miserārum	miserōrum
Dative	miserō	miserae	miserō	miserīs	miserīs	miserīs
Accusative	miserum	miseram	miserum	miserōs	miserās	misera
Ablative	miserō	miserā	miserō	miserīs	miserīs	miserīs

Nominative	pulcher	pulchra	pulchrum	pulchrī	pulchrae	pulchra
Genitive	pulchrī	pulchrae	pulchrī	pulchrōrum	pulchrārum	pulchrōrum
Dative	pulchrō	pulchrae	pulchrō	pulchrīs	pulchrīs	pulchrīs
Accusative	pulchrum	pulchram	pulchrum	pulchrōs	pulchrās	pulchra
Ablative	pulchrō	pulchrā	pulchrō	pulchrīs	pulchrīs	pulchrīs

Latin Workbook - Level 6
Copyright © 2006 by Karen Mohs

APPENDIX

Adjectives (continued)

Third Declension Adjectives - Three Terminations

Adjectives ending in -er in the masculine nominative singular, -is in the feminine, and -e in the neuter are third declension adjectives of three terminations. Third declension adjectives are declined like third declension i-stem nouns. The ablative singular ending (-ī) is like the third declension **neuter** i-stem nouns.

	Singular			*Plural*		
	Masculine	Feminine	Neuter	Masculine	Feminine	Neuter
Nominative	celer	celeris	celere	celerēs	celerēs	celeria
Genitive	celeris	celeris	celeris	celerium	celerium	celerium
Dative	celerī	celerī	celerī	celeribus	celeribus	celeribus
Accusative	celerem	celerem	celere	celerēs	celerēs	celeria
Ablative	celerī	celerī	celerī	celeribus	celeribus	celeribus

Third Declension Adjectives - Two Terminations

Adjectives ending in -is in the masculine and feminine nominative singular, and -e in the neuter are third declension adjectives of two terminations.

	Singular		*Plural*	
	Masculine/Feminine	Neuter	Masculine/Feminine	Neuter
Nominative	omnis	omne	omnēs	omnia
Genitive	omnis	omnis	omnium	omnium
Dative	omnī	omnī	omnibus	omnibus
Accusative	omnem	omne	omnēs	omnia
Ablative	omnī	omnī	omnibus	omnibus

Third Declension Adjectives - One Termination

Adjectives of the third declension whose masculine nominative singular does **not** end in -er or -is are third declension adjectives of one termination. Because the stem cannot be determined from the nominative singular, the genitive singular of these one termination adjectives must be learned.

	Singular		*Plural*	
	Masculine/Feminine	Neuter	Masculine/Feminine	Neuter
Nominative	potēns	potēns	potentēs	potentia
Genitive	potentis	potentis	potentium	potentium
Dative	potentī	potentī	potentibus	potentibus
Accusative	potentem	potēns	potentēs	potentia
Ablative	potentī	potentī	potentibus	potentibus

APPENDIX

Adjectives (continued)

Cardinal Numerals

Cardinal numerals are the most common numerals in Latin.

1 (I) - ūnus, ūna, ūnum	30 (XXX) - trīgintā
2 (II) - duo, duae, duo	40 (XL) - quadrāgintā
3 (III) - trēs, tria	50 (L) - quīnquāgintā
4 (IV) - quattuor	60 (LX) - sexāgintā
5 (V) - quīnque	70 (LXX) - septuāgintā
6 (VI) - sex	80 (LXXX) - octōgintā
7 (VII) - septem	90 (XC) - nōnāgintā
8 (VIII) - octō	
9 (IX) - novem	
10 (X) - decem	100 (C) - centum
11 (XI) - ūndecim	200 (CC) - ducentī, ducentae, ducenta
12 (XII) - duodecim	300 (CCC) - trecentī, -ae, -a
13 (XIII) - tredecim	400 (CCCC) - quadringentī, -ae, -a
14 (XIV) - quattuordecim	500 (D) - quīngentī, -ae, -a
15 (XV) - quīndecim	600 (DC) - sescentī, -ae, -a
16 (XVI) - sēdecim	700 (DCC) - septingentī, -ae, -a
17 (XVII) - septendecim	800 (DCCC) - octingentī, -ae, -a
18 (XVIII) - duodēvīgintī	900 (DCCCC) - nōngentī, -ae, -a
19 (XIX) - ūndēvīgintī	
20 (XX) - vīgintī	
21 (XXI) - vīgintī ūnus (or ūnus et vīgintī)	1000 (M) - mīlle
29 (XXIX) - ūndētrīgintā	2000 (MM) - duo mīlle

Declension of Cardinal Numerals

Latin cardinal numerals from *one* to *three* are declined as shown below. The numerals from *four* through *one hundred* are indeclinable. That is, the forms do not change to indicate gender, number, and case.

	One - ūnus			Two - duo			Three - trēs	
	Masculine	Feminine	Neuter	Masculine	Feminine	Neuter	Masculine/Feminine	Neuter
Nominative	ūnus	ūna	ūnum	duo	duae	duo	trēs	tria
Genitive	ūnīus	ūnīus	ūnīus	duōrum	duārum	duōrum	trium	trium
Dative	ūnī	ūnī	ūnī	duōbus	duābus	duōbus	tribus	tribus
Accusative	ūnum	ūnam	ūnum	duōs	duās	duo	trēs	tria
Ablative	ūnō	ūnā	ūnō	duōbus	duābus	duōbus	tribus	tribus

Latin Workbook - Level 6
Copyright © 2006 by Karen Mohs

APPENDIX

Adjectives (continued)

Ordinal Numerals

Latin ordinal numerals express a position in a sequence.

1st - prīmus, prīma, prīmum

2nd - secundus, -a, -um

3rd - tertius, -a, -um

4th - quārtus, -a, -um

5th - quīntus, -a, -um

6th - sextus, -a, -um

7th - septimus, -a, -um

8th - octāvus, -a, -um

9th - nōnus, -a, -um

10th - decimus, -a, -um

11th - ūndecimus, -a, -um

12th - duodecimus, -a, -um

13th - tertius, -a, -um decimus, -a, -um

14th - quārtus, -a, -um decimus, -a, -um

15th - quīntus, -a, -um decimus, -a, -um

16th - sextus, -a, -um decimus, -a, -um

17th - septimus, -a, -um decimus, -a, -um

18th - duodēvīcēsimus, -a, -um

19th - ūndēvīcēsimus, -a, -um

20th - vīcēsimus, -a, -um

21st - vīcēsimus, -a, -um prīmus, -a, -um

29th - ūndētrīcēsimus, -a, -um

30th - trīcēsimus, -a, -um

40th - quadrāgēsimus, -a, -um

50th - quīnquāgēsimus, -a, -um

60th - sexāgēsimus, -a, -um

70th - septuāgēsimus, -a, -um

80th - octōgēsimus, -a, -um

90th - nōnāgēsimus, -a, -um

100th - centēsimus, -a, -um

200th - ducentēsimus, -a, -um

300th - trecentēsimus, -a, -um

400th - quadringentēsimus, -a, -um

500th - quīngentēsimus, -a, -um

600th - sescentēsimus, -a, -um

700th - septingentēsimus, -a, -um

800th - octingentēsimus, -a, -um

900th - nōngentēsimus, -a, -um

1000th - mīllēsimus, -a, -um

2000th - bis mīllēsimus, -a, -um

Declension of Ordinal Numerals

Latin ordinal numerals are declined like adjectives of the first and second declension.

APPENDIX

Pronouns

A pronoun is a word that takes the place of a noun.

Personal Pronouns - First Person

	Singular	*Meaning*	*Plural*	*Meaning*
Nominative	ego	I	nōs	we
Genitive	meī	of me	nostrī or nostrum	of us
Dative	mihi	to/for me	nōbīs	to/for us
Accusative	mē	me	nōs	us
Ablative	mē	with/by/from me	nōbīs	with/by/from us

To express *possession*, the possessive adjective (meus, if singular; noster, if plural) is used instead of the genitive case of the personal pronoun (meī, if singular; nostrī/nostrum, if plural). The genitive case of first person pronouns is used in other constructions. (See page 93.)

Personal Pronouns - Second Person

	Singular	*Meaning*	*Plural*	*Meaning*
Nominative	tū	you (s.)	vōs	you (pl.)
Genitive	tuī	of you (s.)	vestrī or vestrum	of you (pl.)
Dative	tibi	to/for you (s.)	vōbīs	to/for you (pl.)
Accusative	tē	you (s.)	vōs	you (pl.)
Ablative	tē	with/by/from you (s.)	vōbīs	with/by/from you (pl.)

To express *possession*, the possessive adjective (tuus, if singular; vester, if plural) is used instead of the genitive case of the personal pronoun (tuī, if singular; vestrī/vestrum, if plural). The genitive case of second person pronouns is used in other constructions. (See page 93.)

Demonstrative Pronouns - Third Person - Masculine

	Singular	*Meaning*	*Plural*	*Meaning*
Nominative	is	he	eī or iī	they
Genitive	eius	of him (his)	eōrum	of them (their)
Dative	eī	to/for him	eīs	to/for them
Accusative	eum	him	eōs	them
Ablative	eō	with/by/from him	eīs	with/by/from them

Latin uses demonstrative pronouns to act as third person personal pronouns.

APPENDIX

Pronouns (continued)

Demonstrative Pronouns - Third Person - Feminine

	Singular	Meaning	Plural	Meaning
Nominative	ea	she	eae	they
Genitive	eius	of her (her)	eārum	of them (their)
Dative	eī	to/for her	eīs	to/for them
Accusative	eam	her	eās	them
Ablative	eā	with/by/from her	eīs	with/by/from them

Demonstrative Pronouns - Third Person - Neuter

	Singular	Meaning	Plural	Meaning
Nominative	id	it	ea	they
Genitive	eius	of it (its)	eōrum	of them (their)
Dative	eī	to/for it	eīs	to/for them
Accusative	id	it	ea	them
Ablative	eō	with/by/from it	eīs	with/by/from them

APPENDIX

General Uses of Pronouns

A *pronoun* takes the place of its *antecedent*.

    Example: The son sees the <u>bread</u> and eats <u>it</u>.
                          antecedent   **pronoun**

In Latin, a pronoun must agree with its antecedent in *gender* and *number*.

    Examples: <u>Lūdum</u> nostrum videō et <u>eum</u> sciō.   I see our school and I know it.
         masc. sing. antecedent   **masc. sing. pronoun**

               (Although we must use the masculine pronoun eum in Latin, we translate into English using the neuter pronoun *it*.)

               <u>Vīllam</u> nostram videō et <u>eam</u> sciō.   I see our farmhouse and I know it.
      fem. sing. antecedent   **fem. sing. pronoun**

               (Although we must use the feminine pronoun eam in Latin, we translate into English using the neuter pronoun *it*.)

If a third person (demonstrative) pronoun is used with a noun, it is acting as a demonstrative. It should be translated *this* (plural: *these*) or *that* (plural: *those*).

    Example: Is est prūdēns.   He is wise.
                Is puer est prūdēns.   This (that) boy is wise.

Latin often omits the possessive pronoun (unless it is needed for emphasis or for clarity). When translating into English, the omitted pronoun should be added.

    Example: Patriam dēfendō.   I defend *my* native land.

The case of a Latin pronoun is determined by its use in the sentence.

Nominative case personal pronouns are primarily used for *emphasis*.

Possession is expressed in third person (demonstrative) pronouns by the *genitive case*. This is in contrast to the first and second person in which possession is expressed by the *possessive adjective*.

When using cum with a first or second person pronoun as an *ablative of accompaniment*, the cum is attached to the end of the ablative pronoun as in mēcum, tēcum, nōbīscum, and vōbīscum.

APPENDIX

Index

APPENDIX

Index

Latin Workbook - Level 6
Copyright © 2006 by Karen Mohs

APPENDIX

Index

i-stem noun, masculine and feminine, 22; neuter, 23; See appendix page 220.

i-stem verb, 20; See appendix page 207-209.

idiom, 54, 60, 86, 90.

imperfect indicative, active, 129, 131; "being" verb, 132; passive, 133, 135; See appendix pages 193-197, 199, 202, 205, 208, 211.

imperfect tense indicator, 129, 131, 133, 135; See appendix pages 199, 202, 205, 208, 211.

impersonal verb, 63, 64.

indeclinable numerals, 77; mīlle, if singular, 84; See appendix page 226.

indicative, present active, 15, 20, 24; present passive, 107, 109; imperfect active, 129, 131; imperfect passive, 133, 135; future active, 149, 151, 152; future passive, 153, 155; "being" verb, 24, 132, 152; See appendix pages 193-212.

indirect object of sentence, 16; See appendix page 214.

indirect statement, 57; See appendix page 213.

infinitive, tenses of, 57; present active is second principal part of Latin verb, 57; present passive, 107, 109; future active, 149, 151, 152; future passive rare, 153; complementary, 57, 97, 143; indirect statement, 57; objective, 57; subjective, 57; with impersonal verb, 63; with verbs, 51, 53, 69; with volō and nōlō, 69; See appendix pages 193-198, 200-201, 203-204, 206-207, 209-210, 212-213.

inquam, defective verb, 125; forms of, 125; use in direct quotation, 125.

interrogative adjectives, 38.

irregular, verbs, iuvō, 49; nōlō, 68; sum, 24; volō, 67, 68; adverbs, 42; See appendix pages 194-197.

iubeō, use with infinitive and subject accusative, 51.

knowing verb, 57; See appendix page 213.

learning adjectives, 30.

letter pronunciation, 1; See appendix page 191.

"linking" verb, word order, 27; See appendix pages 194, 214.

location, 18, 41; See appendix page 215.

long by nature, See appendix page 192.

long by position, See appendix page 192.

macron, rules for use, 27; See appendix page 192.

manner, 18; See appendix page 214.

masculine gender, 16, 17, 19, 21, 22, 25, 26, 30, 31, 35; See appendix page 214.

means or instrument, 18; See appendix page 214.

measure, 93; See appendix page 215.

mīlle, indeclinable if singular, 84.

multus, used with another adjective, 11.

-ne, 29.

necesse, defective adjective, 121, 122; use with "being" verb, 121; use with dative case, 111.

neuter gender, 17, 23, 25, 30, 31, 35; See appendix page 214.

nihil, defective noun, 83.

nīl, defective noun, 83.

no question, 29.

nōlō, 67, 68; See appendix page 197.

nominative case, of nouns, 16, 22, 23; of adjectives, 30, 31, 35; pronoun use of for emphasis, 71; See appendix pages 214, 216-226, 228-230.

nominative singular is only one syllable, 22; See appendix page 220.

nōnne, 29.

noun, 16, 17, 19, 21-23, 25, 26; use with demonstrative pronoun, 75; verbal, 57; See appendix pages 212, 214-223.

num, 29.

number, adjective agreement with, 30; agreement of pronoun and antecedent, 75; See appendix pages 194-212, 216-225, 228-230.

numerals, adjective expressing, 38; cardinal, 77; ordinal, 79; See appendix pages 226, 227.

APPENDIX

Index

Latin Workbook - Level 6
Copyright © 2006 by Karen Mohs

APPENDIX

Index

reliquus, genitive not needed, 100.

rēs, definition of, 96.

retention of vowel in stem, of nouns, 17, 19, 21; of adjectives, 31.

***saying* verb**, 57; See appendix page 213.

second conjugation, present active indicative, 15; present passive indicative, 107; imperfect active indicative, 129; imperfect passive indicative, 133; future active indicative, 149; future passive indicative, 153; See appendix pages 201-203.

second declension, of nouns, masculine, 17, 19; neuter, 23; of adjectives, 30, 31; See appendix pages 216-218, 224.

second person personal pronoun, 71; order in sentence, 74; See appendix page 228.

semi-deponent, 61; lacking fourth principal part, 61.

sentence, direct object of, 16; indirect object of, 16; possession, 16; subject of, 16; See appendix page 214.

separation, 111; See appendix page 215.

special case uses, 18, 41, 111; See appendix pages 214-215.

special consonant sounds, 1; See appendix page 191.

statement, indirect, 57; See appendix page 213.

stem, of verbs, 15, 20, 24; of nouns, 16, 17, 19, 21, 22, 25, 26; of adjectives for adverbs, 42; See appendix pages 198-212, 216-225.

subject, accusative case, 51, 69; infinitive functions as, 57; of impersonal verb, 63; of sentence, 16; See appendix page 214.

subjective infinitive, 57; See appendix page 213.

substantive use of adjectives, 30.

sum, present indicative, 24; imperfect indicative, 132; future indicative, 152; with necesse, 121; See appendix page 194.

syllable, length of, 28; names of, 28; rules of division, 28; same number of in nominative and genitive cases, 22; See appendix pages 192, 220.

temptō, use with infinitive, 57; See appendix page 213.

tense, See *present indicative*, *imperfect indicative*, etc.

tense indicator, imperfect, 129, 131, 133, 135; future, 149, 151-153, 155; See appendix pages 199, 200, 202, 203, 205, 206, 208, 209, 211, 212.

tense of infinitive, 57; See appendix page 212.

terminations of adjectives, 35; See appendix page 225.

***thinking* verb**, 57; See appendix page 213.

third conjugation, present active indicative, 20; present passive indicative, 109; imperfect active indicative, 131; imperfect passive indicative, 135; future active indicative, 151; future passive indicative, 155; See appendix pages 204-206.

third conjugation i-stem, present active indicative, 20; present passive indicative, 109; imperfect active indicative, 131; imperfect passive indicative, 135; future active indicative, 151; future passive indicative, 155; See appendix pages 207-209.

third declension, of nouns, masculine and feminine, 21; masculine and feminine i-stem, 22; neuter, 23; of adjectives, 35; See appendix pages 219-221, 225.

third person personal pronoun, demonstrative pronoun, 73; order in sentence, 74; See appendix pages 228-229.

time when, 111; See appendix page 215.

time within which, 111; See appendix page 215.

ultima, 28; See appendix page 192.

verb, 15, 20, 24; deponent, 61, 137, 139, 141; impersonal, 63; infinitive similar to, 57; irregular principal parts, 24, 49, 53, 67, 68; *knowing*, 57; last in sentence, 27; of motion, 87; *perceiving and feeling*, 57; principal parts, 15; *saying*, 57; semi-deponent, 61; *thinking*, 57; use with infinitive and subject accusative, 51, 69; See appendix pages 193-213.

verbal noun, 57; See appendix page 212.

APPENDIX

Index

voice, of verb, 107; of infinitive, 57; See appendix
    pages 193, 212.
volō, 67, 68; See appendix page 196.
vowels, 1; retention in noun stem, 17, 19, 21; retention
    in adjective stem, 31; See appendix pages 191, 217,
    224.

whole, genitive of the, 93; See appendix page 215.
word order, 27; adjective expressing numerals, 38;
    adjective expressing quantity, 38;
    adjective-genitive-noun construction, 46;
    adjective-noun-adjective construction, 46;
    adjective-noun-possessive adjective construction,
    46; cum with adjective and noun, 18; emphatic
    adjective, 38; interrogative adjective, 38; See
    appendix page 214.

yes or **no** *question*, 29.
yes *question*, 29.

APPENDIX

Flashcard Tips

1. Remember to practice flashcards daily.

2. Do not move ahead in the workbook if you are struggling for mastery. Review the flashcards every day until you are confident and ready to learn more.

3. For each noun, you must continue to learn both the nominative and the genitive forms, as well as the gender. As cards are flashed, note the ending on the genitive form. Identify the declension based on the genitive ending. For example, if the genitive form ends in -ae, the noun belongs to the first declension. If it ends in -ī, the noun belongs to the second declension, etc. (See the grammar review pages for each declension.)

4. For each verb, you must continue to learn all four principal parts. As cards are flashed, note the ending on the second principal part. Identify the conjugation based on that ending. For example, if the second principal part ends in -āre, the verb belongs to the first conjugation, etc. (See the grammar review pages.)

5. You should thoroughly learn each conjugation and declension card. This will require extra effort, but will greatly enhance understanding. Please apply the endings on these cards to all appropriate vocabulary words.

6. When the number of the cards becomes too cumbersome to review in one day, remove the cards you know without hesitation and put them in an "Occasional Practice" stack. Review the "Occasional Practice" stack once a week.

(front)	(back)
Occasionally review the vocabulary cards from the Level Four and Level Five flashcard decks. The Latin Level Four and Level Five decks include all vocabulary taught in *Latin's Not So Tough!* Levels Two through Five.	(Level 6)
principal parts of a verb (amō)	(Start on page 15.) (Level 6) amō amāre amāvī amātum
first conjugation present active indicative	(Page 15) (Level 6) amō — I like amāmus — we like amās — you (sing.) like amātis — you (pl.) like amat — he (she, it) likes amant — they like
second conjugation present active indicative	(Page 15) (Level 6) sedeō — I sit sedēmus — we sit sedēs — you (sing.) sit sedētis — you (pl.) sit sedet — he (she, it) sits sedent — they sit
first declension (singular)	(Page 16) (Level 6) cūra — the care cūrae — of the care cūrae — to/for the care cūram — the care cum cūrā — with care
first declension (plural)	(Page 16) (Level 6) cūrae — the cares cūrārum — of the cares cūrīs — to/for the cares cūrās — the cares cum cūrīs — with cares

(front)	(back)
second declension (singular)	(Page 17) (Level 6) lūdus — the school lūdī — of the school lūdō — to/for the school lūdum — the school in lūdō — in the school
second declension (plural)	(Page 17) (Level 6) lūdī — the schools lūdōrum — of the schools lūdīs — to/for the schools lūdōs — the schools in lūdīs — in the schools
second declension -ius (singular)	(Page 17) (Level 6) gladius — the sword gladī — of the sword gladiō — to/for the sword gladium — the sword gladiō — with the sword
second declension -ius (plural)	(Page 17) (Level 6) gladiī — the swords gladiōrum — of the swords gladiīs — to/for the swords gladiōs — the swords gladiīs — with the swords
In īnsulā puella habitat. is an "Ablative of _____." It means _____.	(Page 18) (Level 6) Place Where The girl lives *on the island.*
Sub vīllā animal habitat. is an "Ablative of _____." It means _____.	(Page 18) (Level 6) Place Where The animal lives *under the villa.*

(front)	(back)
Puellās tubā convocō. is an "Ablative of _____." It means _____.	(Page 18) (Level 6) Means or Instrument I summon the girls *with the trumpet*.
Cum audāciā pugnō. is an "Ablative of _____." It means _____.	(Page 18) (Level 6) Manner I fight *with boldness*.
Cum fēminā puella ambulat. is an "Ablative of _____." It means _____.	(Page 18) (Level 6) Accompaniment The girl walks *with the woman*.
second declension -er (singular) as in puer	(Page 19) (Level 6) puer — the boy puerī — of the boy puerō — to/for the boy puerum — the boy cum puerō — with the boy
second declension -er (plural) as in puer	(Page 19) (Level 6) puerī — the boys puerōrum — of the boys puerīs — to/for the boys puerōs — the boys cum puerīs — with the boys
second declension -er (singular) as in ager	(Page 19) (Level 6) ager — the field agrī — of the field agrō — to/for the field agrum — the field in agrō — in the field

(front)	(back)

second declension -er (plural) as in **ager**	(Page 19) (Level 6) agrī the fields agrōrum of the fields agrīs to/for the fields agrōs the fields in agrīs in the fields
third conjugation present active indicative	(Page 20) (Level 6) dīcō I say dīcimus we say dīcis you (sing.) say dīcitis you (pl.) say dīcit he (she, it) says dīcunt they say
third conjugation i-stem present active indicative	(Page 20) (Level 6) capiō I take capimus we take capis you (sing.) take capitis you (pl.) take capit he (she, it) takes capiunt they take
third declension (singular) as in **soror**	(Page 21) (Level 6) soror the sister sorōris of the sister sorōrī to/for the sister sorōrem the sister cum sorōre with the sister
third declension (plural) as in **soror**	(Page 21) (Level 6) sorōrēs the sisters sorōrum of the sisters sorōribus to/for the sisters sorōrēs the sisters cum sorōribus with the sisters
third declension (singular) as in **frāter**	(Page 21) (Level 6) frāter the brother frātris of the brother frātrī to/for the brother frātrem the brother cum frātre with the brother

(front)	(back)

<table>
<tr>
<td>third declension
(plural)
as in frāter</td>
<td>(Page 21)   (Level 6)

frātrēs   the brothers
frātrum   of the brothers
frātribus   to/for the brothers
frātrēs   the brothers
cum frātribus   with the brothers</td>
</tr>
<tr>
<td>third declension i-stem
(singular)
as in hostis</td>
<td>(Page 22)   (Level 6)

hostis   the enemy
hostis   of the enemy
hostī   to/for the enemy
hostem   the enemy
cum hoste   with the enemy</td>
</tr>
<tr>
<td>third declension i-stem
(plural)
as in hostis</td>
<td>(Page 22)   (Level 6)

hostēs   the enemies
hostium   of the enemies
hostibus   to/for the enemies
hostēs   the enemies
cum hostibus   with the enemies</td>
</tr>
<tr>
<td>third declension i-stem
(singular)
as in gēns</td>
<td>(Page 22)   (Level 6)

gēns   the nation
gentis   of the nation
gentī   to/for the nation
gentem   the nation
cum gente   with the nation</td>
</tr>
<tr>
<td>third declension i-stem
(plural)
as in gēns</td>
<td>(Page 22)   (Level 6)

gentēs   the nations
gentium   of the nations
gentibus   to/for the nations
gentēs   the nations
cum gentibus   with the nations</td>
</tr>
<tr>
<td>third declension i-stem
(singular)
as in urbs</td>
<td>(Page 22)   (Level 6)

urbs   the city
urbis   of the city
urbī   to/for the city
urbem   the city
in urbe   in the city</td>
</tr>
</table>

(front)	(back)
third declension i-stem (plural) as in **urbs**	(Page 22) (Level 6) urbēs — the cities urbium — of the cities urbibus — to/for the cities urbēs — the cities in urbibus — in the cities
second declension neuter (singular)	(Page 23) (Level 6) caelum — the sky caelī — of the sky caelō — to/for the sky caelum — the sky in caelō — in the sky
second declension neuter (plural)	(Page 23) (Level 6) caela — the skies caelōrum — of the skies caelīs — to/for the skies caela — the skies in caelīs — in the skies
third declension neuter (singular)	(Page 23) (Level 6) nōmen — the name nōminis — of the name nōminī — to/for the name nōmen — the name nōmine — with the name
third declension neuter (plural)	(Page 23) (Level 6) nōmina — the names nōminum — of the names nōminibus — to/for the names nōmina — the names nōminibus — with the names
third declension i-stem neuter (singular)	(Page 23) (Level 6) mare — the sea maris — of the sea marī — to/for the sea mare — the sea in marī — in the sea

(front)	(back)
third declension i-stem neuter (plural)	(Page 23) (Level 6) maria the seas marium of the seas maribus to/for the seas maria the seas in maribus in the seas
fourth conjugation present active indicative	(Page 24) (Level 6) audiō I hear audīmus we hear audīs you (sing.) hear audītis you (pl.) hear audit he (she, it) hears audiunt they hear
the being verb present indicative	(Page 24) (Level 6) sum I am sumus we are es you (sing.) are estis you (pl.) are est he (she, it) is, sunt they are, there are there is
fourth declension (singular)	(Page 25) (Level 6) manus the hand manūs of the hand manuī to/for the hand manum the hand in manū in the hand
fourth declension (plural)	(Page 25) (Level 6) manūs the hands manuum of the hands manibus to/for the hands manūs the hands in manibus in the hands
fourth declension neuter (singular)	(Page 25) (Level 6) cornū the horn cornūs of the horn cornū to/for the horn cornū the horn cornū with the horn

(front)	(back)
fourth declension neuter (plural)	(Page 25) (Level 6) cornua — the horns cornuum — of the horns cornibus — to/for the horns cornua — the horns cornibus — with the horns
fifth declension (singular) as in diēs	(Page 26) (Level 6) diēs — the day diēī — of the day diēī — to/for the day diem — the day diē — by means of the day
fifth declension (plural) as in diēs	(Page 26) (Level 6) diēs — the days diērum — of the days diēbus — to/for the days diēs — the days diēbus — by means of the days
fifth declension (singular) as in spēs	(Page 26) (Level 6) spēs — the hope speī — of the hope speī — to/for the hope spem — the hope spē — by means of the hope
fifth declension (plural) as in spēs	(Page 26) (Level 6) spēs — the hopes spērum — of the hopes spēbus — to/for the hopes spēs — the hopes spēbus — by means of the hopes
1. A vowel always has a macron before which letters? 2. A vowel never has a macron before which letters? 3. In most fifth declension words, when the vowel -e- comes after another vowel, does it have a macron? 4. What three letters, if **last** in a word, usually keep the vowel before that final letter short?	(Page 27) (Level 6) 1. -ns 2. -nt 3. yes 4. m r t

(front)	(back)
Syllables: e pis tu la 　 3　 2　 1	(Page 28)　　　　　　　　　(Level 6) 1. ultima 2. penult 3. antepenult
1. When is a syllable long by **nature**? 2. When is a syllable long by **position**?	(Page 28)　　　　　　　　　(Level 6) 1. when it contains a long vowel or a diphthong 2. when its vowel is followed by two or more consonants or by a double consonant (x or z)
1. On two-syllable words, which syllable is accented? 2. On three-syllable words with a long penult, which syllable is accented? 3. On three-syllable words with a short penult, which syllable is accented?	(Page 28)　　　　　　　　　(Level 6) 1. the penult 2. the penult 3. the antepenult
1. How do you ask a question that expects a *yes* or *no* answer? 2. How do you ask a question that expects a *yes* answer? 3. How do you ask a question that expects a *no* answer?	(Page 29)　　　　　　　　　(Level 6) 1. add -ne to the end of the first word in the sentence 2. begin the sentence with the word nōnne 3. begin the sentence with the word num
singular adjectives (first and second declension) **as in bonus**	(Page 30)　　　　　　　　　(Level 6) bonus　　bona　　bonum bonī　　　bonae　　bonī bonō　　　bonae　　bonō bonum　　bonam　　bonum bonō　　　bonā　　bonō
plural adjectives (first and second declension) **as in bonus**	(Page 30)　　　　　　　　　(Level 6) bonī　　　bonae　　bona bonōrum　bonārum　bonōrum bonīs　　bonīs　　bonīs bonōs　　bonās　　bona bonīs　　bonīs　　bonīs

(front)	(back)
singular adjectives (first and second declension) as in **miser**	(Page 31) (Level 6) miser misera miserum miserī miserae miserī miserō miserae miserō miserum miseram miserum miserō miserā miserō
plural adjectives (first and second declension) as in **miser**	(Page 31) (Level 6) miserī miserae misera miserōrum miserārum miserōrum miserīs miserīs miserīs miserōs miserās misera miserīs miserīs miserīs
singular adjectives (first and second declension) as in **pulcher**	(Page 31) (Level 6) pulcher pulchra pulchrum pulchrī pulchrae pulchrī pulchrō pulchrae pulchrō pulchrum pulchram pulchrum pulchrō pulchrā pulchrō
plural adjectives (first and second declension) as in **pulcher**	(Page 31) (Level 6) pulchrī pulchrae pulchra pulchrōrum pulchrārum pulchrōrum pulchrīs pulchrīs pulchrīs pulchrōs pulchrās pulchra pulchrīs pulchrīs pulchrīs
singular adjectives (third declension) **three terminations**	(Page 35) (Level 6) celer celeris celere celeris celeris celeris celerī celerī celerī celerem celerem celere celerī celerī celerī
plural adjectives (third declension) **three terminations**	(Page 35) (Level 6) celerēs celerēs celeria celerium celerium celerium celeribus celeribus celeribus celerēs celerēs celeria celeribus celeribus celeribus

(front)	(back)
singular adjectives (third declension) **two terminations**	(Page 35) (Level 6) omnis — omne omnis — omnis omnī — omnī omnem — omne omnī — omnī
plural adjectives (third declension) **two terminations**	(Page 35) (Level 6) omnēs — omnia omnium — omnium omnibus — omnibus omnēs — omnia omnibus — omnibus
singular adjectives (third declension) **one termination**	(Page 35) (Level 6) potēns — potēns potentis — potentis potentī — potentī potentem — potēns potentī — potentī
plural adjectives (third declension) **one termination**	(Page 35) (Level 6) potentēs — potentia potentium — potentium potentibus — potentibus potentēs — potentia potentibus — potentibus
In vīllam puella ambulat. is an "Accusative of _____." It means _____.	(Page 41) (Level 6) Place to Which The girl walks *into the villa*.
Ad vīllam puella ambulat. is an "Accusative of _____." It means _____.	(Page 41) (Level 6) Place to Which The girl walks *to the villa*.

(front)	(back)
Sub vīllam puella ambulat. _____ is an "Accusative of _____." It means _____.	(Page 41) (Level 6) Place to Which The girl walks *up to the villa.*
līber	(Page 45) (Level 6) lībera līberum (adjective) free
līberī	(Page 45) (Level 6) līberōrum children
mox	(Page 45) (Level 6) (adverb) soon
rēgnō	(Page 45) (Level 6) rēgnāre rēgnāvī rēgnātum reign, dominate, rule
carmen	(Page 45) (Level 6) carminis (n.) song, poem

(front)	(back)
summus	(Page 47) (Level 6) summa summum (adjective) **highest, top of, greatest, chief**
summē	(Page 47) (Level 6) (adverb) **very, intensely, extremely**
novus	(Page 47) (Level 6) nova novum (adjective) **new**
novē	(Page 47) (Level 6) (adverb) **newly**
flūmen	(Page 47) (Level 6) flūminis (n.) **flowing, river, stream**
dum	(Page 47) (Level 6) (conjunction) **while, until, as long as**

(front)	(back)
iuvō	(Page 49)　　　　(Level 6) iuvāre iūvī iūtum help, do good to, favor
plēnus	(Page 49)　　　　(Level 6) plēna plēnum (adjective) full
plēnē	(Page 49)　　　　(Level 6) (adverb) fully, completely
grātus	(Page 49)　　　　(Level 6) grāta grātum (adjective) pleasing, welcome, thankful
grātē	(Page 49)　　　　(Level 6) (adverb) gratefully, pleasantly, willingly
iniūria	(Page 49)　　　　(Level 6) iniūriae (f.) injustice, insult, injury

(front)	(back)
cōgō	(Page 51) (Level 6) cōgere coēgī coāctum collect, compel
vōx	(Page 51) (Level 6) vōcis (f.) voice
prohibeō	(Page 51) (Level 6) prohibēre prohibuī prohibitum prevent, hold back, keep ... from
iubeō	(Page 51) (Level 6) iubēre iussī iussum order, command, bid
dēbeō	(Page 53) (Level 6) dēbēre dēbuī dēbitum owe, ought
grātiam dēbeō	(Page 53) (Level 6) I am under an obligation

(front)	(back)
vērus	(Page 53) (Level 6) vēra vērum (adjective) true
vērē	(Page 53) (Level 6) (adverb) really, truly
possum	(Page 53) (Level 6) posse potuī can, be able
bellum	(Page 53) (Level 6) bellī (n.) war
What is an infinitive? What does this mean?	(Page 57) (Level 6) verbal noun It acts in some ways like a *noun* (it can function as a subject or as an object), but it is also like a *verb* (it has tense and voice).
In the sentence Vidēre est scīre, vidēre is "_ _____ Infinitive." The sentence means _____.	(Page 57) (Level 6) a Subjective *To see* is to know.

.

(front)	(back)
In the sentence **Cupit edere,** edere is "_ _____ Infinitive." The sentence means _____.	(Page 57) (Level 6) a Complementary He wants *to eat*.
Name some verbs that may require a **Complementary Infinitive** to complete their meaning.	(Page 57) (Level 6) parō, cupiō, cōnstituō, temptō, dēbeō, possum, prohibeō, etc.
In the sentence **Iubet virōs edere,** edere is "_ _____ Infinitive." The sentence means _____.	(Page 57) (Level 6) an Objective He orders the men *to eat*.
In an **Objective Infinitive**, the *subject* of the infinitive is in the _____ case.	(Page 57) (Level 6) accusative
Name some verbs that are commonly used with an **Objective Infinitive**.	(Page 57) (Level 6) iubeō, cōgō, prohibeō, etc.
The sentence **Vir dīcit puerum edere** is "_ _____ Statement." The sentence means _____.	(Page 57) (Level 6) an Indirect The man says that the boy eats.

(front)	(back)
In an **Indirect Statement**, the *subject* of the infinitive is in the _____ case.	(Page 57) (Level 6) accusative
Name some **saying** verbs that are commonly used with an **Indirect Statement**.	(Page 57) (Level 6) dīcō, nūntiō, nārrō, scrībō, doceō, dēmōnstrō, moneō, etc.
Name some **knowing** verbs that are commonly used with an **Indirect Statement**.	(Page 57) (Level 6) sciō, memoriā teneō, etc.
Name some **thinking** verbs that are commonly used with an **Indirect Statement**.	(Page 57) (Level 6) cernō, cōgitō, crēdō, habeō, putō, spērō, etc.
Name some **perceiving** and **feeling** verbs that are commonly used with an **Indirect Statement**.	(Page 57) (Level 6) videō, audiō, etc.
caput	(Page 59) (Level 6) capitis (n.) head

(front)	(back)
propter	(Page 59) (Level 6) (preposition - used with the accusative case) **because of, on account of**
ignis	(Page 59) (Level 6) ignis (m.) **fire**
grātia	(Page 59) (Level 6) grātiae (f.) **gratitude, influence, favor**
grātiam habeō	(Page 59) (Level 6) **I feel gratitude**
tempus	(Page 61) (Level 6) temporis (n.) **time**
audeō	(Page 61) (Level 6) audēre ausus sum **dare**

(front)	(back)
amīcus	(Page 61) (Level 6) amīca amīcum (adjective) **friendly**
amīcē	(Page 61) (Level 6) (adverb) **in a friendly way**
nāvis	(Page 61) (Level 6) nāvis (f.) **ship**
parātus	(Page 63) (Level 6) parāta parātum (adjective) **ready, prepared**
parātē	(Page 63) (Level 6) (adverb) **carefully, promptly, readily**
licet	(Page 63) (Level 6) (impersonal verb - used with the dative case) **it is permitted**

(front)	(back)
oportet	(Page 63) (Level 6) (impersonal verb - used with the accusative case) it is necessary, it is proper
iūs	(Page 63) (Level 6) iūris (n.) right, law, justice
aestās	(Page 65) (Level 6) aestātis (f.) summer
gubernō	(Page 65) (Level 6) gubernāre gubernāvī gubernātum steer, navigate, govern
fugiō	(Page 65) (Level 6) fugere fūgī fugitum flee, flee from, avoid
hiems	(Page 65) (Level 6) hiemis (f.) winter

(front)	(back)
volō	(Page 67) (Level 6) velle voluī wish, want, be willing
nōlō	(Page 67) (Level 6) nōlle nōluī not wish, be unwilling
incipiō	(Page 67) (Level 6) incipere incēpī inceptum begin
cīvis	(Page 67) (Level 6) cīvis (m. or f.) citizen
first person pronouns singular	(Page 71) (Level 6) ego — I meī — of me mihi — to/for me mē — me mē — with/by/from me
first person pronouns plural	(Page 71) (Level 6) nōs — we nostrī (nostrum) — of us nōbīs — to/for us nōs — us nōbīs — with/by/from us

(front)	(back)
second person pronouns singular	(Page 71)　　　　　　　　　　　　(Level 6) tū　　　　　　you (s.) tuī　　　　　of you (s.) tibi　　　　　to/for you (s.) tē　　　　　　you (s.) tē　　　　　　with/by/from you (s.)
second person pronouns plural	(Page 71)　　　　　　　　　　　　(Level 6) vōs　　　　　　　　　you (pl.) vestrī (vestrum)　　of you (pl.) vōbīs　　　　　　　to/for you (pl.) vōs　　　　　　　　you (pl.) vōbīs　　　　　　　with/by/from you (pl.)
demonstrative pronouns (third person pronouns) singular (masculine)	(Page 73)　　　　　　　　　　　　(Level 6) is　　　　　he eius　　　of him (his) eī　　　　to/for him eum　　　him eō　　　　with/by/from him
demonstrative pronouns (third person pronouns) plural (masculine)	(Page 73)　　　　　　　　　　　　(Level 6) eī (iī)　　　they eōrum　　　of them (their) eīs　　　　　to/for them eōs　　　　　them eīs　　　　　with/by/from them
demonstrative pronouns (third person pronouns) singular (feminine)	(Page 73)　　　　　　　　　　　　(Level 6) ea　　　　she eius　　　of her (her) eī　　　　to/for her eam　　　her eā　　　　with/by/from her
demonstrative pronouns (third person pronouns) plural (feminine)	(Page 73)　　　　　　　　　　　　(Level 6) eae　　　　they eārum　　　of them (their) eīs　　　　　to/for them eās　　　　　them eīs　　　　　with/by/from them

(front)	(back)
demonstrative pronouns (third person pronouns) singular (neuter)	(Page 73) (Level 6) id — it eius — of it (its) eī — to/for it id — it eō — with/by/from it
demonstrative pronouns (third person pronouns) plural (neuter)	(Page 73) (Level 6) ea — they eōrum — of them (their) eīs — to/for them ea — them eīs — with/by/from them
cardinal numerals 1-10	(Page 77) (Level 6) 1 (I) - ūnus, ūna, ūnum 6 (VI) - sex 2 (II) - duo, duae, duo 7 (VII) - septem 3 (III) - trēs, tria 8 (VIII) - octō 4 (IV) - quattuor 9 (IX) - novem 5 (V) - quīnque 10 (X) - decem
cardinal numerals 11-20	(Page 77) (Level 6) 11 (XI) - ūndecim 16 (XVI) - sēdecim 12 (XII) - duodecim 17 (XVII) - septendecim 13 (XIII) - tredecim 18 (XVIII) - duodēvigintī 14 (XIV) - quattuordecim 19 (XIX) - ūndēvigintī 15 (XV) - quīndecim 20 (XX) - vīgintī
cardinal numerals 100 and 1000	(Page 77) (Level 6) 100 (C) - centum 1000 (M) - mīlle
cardinal numeral **one** declension	(Page 77) (Level 6) ūnus ūna ūnum ūnīus ūnīus ūnīus ūnī ūnī ūnī ūnum ūnam ūnum ūnō ūnā ūnō

(front)	(back)
cardinal numeral **two** declension	(Page 77) (Level 6) duo duae duo duōrum duārum duōrum duōbus duābus duōbus duōs duās duo duōbus duābus duōbus
cardinal numeral **three** declension	(Page 77) (Level 6) trēs tria trium trium tribus tribus trēs tria tribus tribus
ordinal numerals 1st-10th	(Page 79) (Level 6) *1st* - prīmus *6th* - sextus *2nd* - secundus *7th* - septimus *3rd* - tertius *8th* - octāvus *4th* - quārtus *9th* - nōnus *5th* - quīntus *10th* - decimus
ordinal numerals 11th-20th	(Page 79) (Level 6) *11th* - ūndecimus *16th* - sextus decimus *12th* - duodecimus *17th* - septimus decimus *13th* - tertius decimus *18th* - duodēvīcēsimus *14th* - quārtus decimus *19th* - ūndēvīcēsimus *15th* - quīntus decimus *20th* - vīcēsimus
ordinal numerals 100th and 1000th	(Page 79) (Level 6) *100th* - centēsimus *1000th* - mīllēsimus
antīquus	(Page 81) (Level 6) **antīqua antiquum** (adjective) ancient, old, former

(front)	(back)
antīquē	(Page 81) (Level 6) (adverb) in former times
prō	(Page 81) (Level 6) (preposition - used with the ablative case) in front of, for, before, on behalf of, instead of
errō	(Page 81) (Level 6) errāre errāvī errātum wander, be mistaken, err
timeō	(Page 81) (Level 6) timēre timuī - fear, be afraid
nihil	(Page 83) (Level 6) (n.) (defective noun) nothing
nīl	(Page 83) (Level 6) (n.) (defective noun) nothing

(front)	(back)
oculus	(Page 83)　　　(Level 6) oculī (m.) eye
mōs	(Page 83)　　　(Level 6) mōris (m.) custom, habit
mōrēs	(Page 83)　　　(Level 6) (mōrum) habits, character
timor	(Page 83)　　　(Level 6) timōris (m.) fear
lūx	(Page 85)　　　(Level 6) lūcis (f.) light
prīmā lūce	(Page 85)　　　(Level 6) at daybreak

(front)	(back)
spīrō	(Page 85) (Level 6) spīrāre spīrāvī spīrātum breathe, blow, exhale
claudō	(Page 85) (Level 6) claudere clausī clausum shut, close
iungō	(Page 85) (Level 6) iungere iūnxī iūnctum join
inimīcus	(Page 87) (Level 6) inimīcī (m.) (personal) enemy
hūmānus	(Page 87) (Level 6) hūmāna hūmānum (adjective) human, refined, cultivated
hūmānē	(Page 87) (Level 6) (adverb) politely, gently

(front)	(back)
pervenio	(Page 87) (Level 6) pervenīre pervēnī perventum reach, arrive at
inimīcus	(Page 87) (Level 6) inimīca inimīcum (adjective) unfriendly, hostile
inimīcē	(Page 87) (Level 6) (adverb) with hostility
pēs	(Page 89) (Level 6) pedis (m.) foot
niger	(Page 89) (Level 6) nigra nigrum (adjective) black
spērō	(Page 89) (Level 6) spērāre spērāvī spērātum hope

(front)	(back)
albus	(Page 89) (Level 6) **alba album** (adjective) white
timor mortis is "_ _____ Genitive." It means _____.	(Page 93) (Level 6) an Objective the fear *of death*
multitūdō hominum is "_ _____ Genitive." It means _____.	(Page 93) (Level 6) a Partitive (Genitive of the Whole) a great number *of men*
liber magnae vēritātis is a "Genitive of _____." It means _____.	(Page 93) (Level 6) Description (Genitive of Measure) the book *of great truth*
liber magnā vēritāte is an "Ablative of _____." It means _____.	(Page 93) (Level 6) Description the book *of great truth*
paucī	(Page 95) (Level 6) **paucae pauca** (adjective) few, a few

(front)	(back)
rēs	(Page 95) (Level 6) reī (f.) thing, matter, affair
rēs novae	(Page 95) (Level 6) revolution
rēs pūblica	(Page 95) (Level 6) state, government, republic
pūblicus	(Page 95) (Level 6) pūblica pūblicum (adjective) public, belonging to the people
pūblicē	(Page 95) (Level 6) (adverb) publicly, officially
herba	(Page 95) (Level 6) herbae (f.) grass

(front)	(back)
falsus	(Page 97) (Level 6) falsa falsum (adjective) false, feigned, deceptive
falsē	(Page 97) (Level 6) (adverb) falsely
pars	(Page 97) (Level 6) partis (f.) part, share, direction
magna pars	(Page 97) (Level 6) majority, greater part
dubitō	(Page 97) (Level 6) dubitāre dubitāvī dubitātum doubt, hesitate
mōns	(Page 97) (Level 6) montis (m.) mountain, hill

(front)	(back)
fēlīcitās	(Page 99) (Level 6) fēlīcitātis (f.) good luck, prosperity
vulnus	(Page 99) (Level 6) vulneris (n.) wound
lūna	(Page 99) (Level 6) lūnae (f.) moon
reliquus	(Page 99) (Level 6) reliqua reliquum (adjective) remaining, the rest of
sōl	(Page 101) (Level 6) sōlis (m.) sun
excēdō	(Page 101) (Level 6) excēdere excessī excessum leave, go out

(front)	(back)
corpus	(Page 101) (Level 6) corporis (n.) body
officium	(Page 101) (Level 6) officī (n.) duty
impedīmentum	(Page 103) (Level 6) impedīmentī (n.) hindrance, impediment
impedīmenta	(Page 103) (Level 6) impedīmentōrum baggage
putō	(Page 103) (Level 6) putāre putāvī putātum think
pāx	(Page 103) (Level 6) pācis (f.) peace

(front)	(back)
crēdō	(Page 103) (Level 6) crēdere crēdidī crēditum believe, trust

Name the voices
of the Latin verb.
Describe each one.
	(Page 107) (Level 6)
	
	Active Voice: The subject of the sentence is *doing an action*.
	    Example: The man loves the woman.
	
	Passive Voice: The subject is *receiving an action*.
	    Example: The man is being loved by the woman.

first conjugation present passive indicative	(Page 107) (Level 6) amor — I am [being] loved amāmur — we are [being] loved amāris — you (s.) are [being] loved amāminī — you (pl.) are [being] loved amātur — he (she, it) is [being] loved amantur — they are [being] loved
first conjugation present passive infinitive	(Page 107) (Level 6) amārī to be loved
second conjugation present passive indicative	(Page 107) (Level 6) moneor — I am [being] warned monēmur — we are [being] warned monēris — you (s.) are [being] warned monēminī — you (pl.) are [being] warned monētur — he (she, it) is [being] warned monentur — they are [being] warned
second conjugation present passive infinitive	(Page 107) (Level 6) monērī to be warned

(front)	(back)
third conjugation present passive indicative	(Page 109) (Level 6) dīcor — I am [being] told dīcimur — we are [being] told dīceris — you (s.) are [being] told dīciminī — you (pl.) are [being] told dīcitur — he (she, it) is [being] told dīcuntur — they are [being] told
third conjugation present passive infinitive	(Page 109) (Level 6) dīcī to be told
third conjugation i-stem present passive indicative	(Page 109) (Level 6) capior — I am [being] taken capimur — we are [being] taken caperis — you (s.) are [being] taken capiminī — you (pl.) are [being] taken capitur — he (she, it) is [being] taken capiuntur — they are [being] taken
third conjugation i-stem present passive infinitive	(Page 109) (Level 6) capī to be taken
fourth conjugation present passive indicative	(Page 109) (Level 6) audior — I am [being] heard audīmur — we are [being] heard audīris — you (s.) are [being] heard audīminī — you (pl.) are [being] heard audītur — he (she, it) is [being] heard audiuntur — they are [being] heard
fourth conjugation present passive infinitive	(Page 109) (Level 6) audīrī to be heard

(front)	(back)
Puella ab urbe currit. is an "Ablative of _____ ." It means _____ .	(Page 111) (Level 6) Place From Which The girl runs *away from the city*.
Dē viā venit. is an "Ablative of _____ ." It means _____ .	(Page 111) (Level 6) Place From Which He comes *down from the road*.
Mē ex agrō portat. is an "Ablative of _____ ." It means _____ .	(Page 111) (Level 6) Place From Which He carries me *out of the field*.
Ā puellā vocātur. is an "Ablative of _____ ." It means _____ .	(Page 111) (Level 6) Personal Agent He is called *by the girl*.
Dux mē ab urbe prohibet. is an "Ablative of _____ ." It means _____ .	(Page 111) (Level 6) Separation The guide keeps me *away from the city*.
Dux mē cūrā līberat. is an "Ablative of _____ ." It means _____ .	(Page 111) (Level 6) Separation The guide frees me *from anxiety*.

(front)	(back)
Secundā hōrā venit. is an "Ablative of _____ ." It means _____ .	(Page 111) (Level 6) Time When He comes *at the second hour.*
Duōbus annīs venit. is an "Ablative of _____ ." It means _____ .	(Page 111) (Level 6) Time Within Which He comes *within two years.*
ūsque	(Page 117) (Level 6) (adverb) all the way, all the time, even
bibō	(Page 117) (Level 6) bibere bibī - drink
stella	(Page 117) (Level 6) stellae (f.) star
mēns	(Page 117) (Level 6) mentis (f.) mind, thought

(front)	(back)
certus	(Page 119) (Level 6) certa certum (adjective) sure, certain, reliable, diligent
certē	(Page 119) (Level 6) (adverb) certainly, surely
ventus	(Page 119) (Level 6) ventī (m.) wind
salūs	(Page 119) (Level 6) salūtis (f.) safety, welfare, greeting
incertus	(Page 119) (Level 6) incerta incertum (adjective) unsure, uncertain, doubtful
incertē	(Page 119) (Level 6) (adverb) uncertainly

(front)	(back)
probō	(Page 121) (Level 6) probāre probāvī probātum prove, approve of, test
opus	(Page 121) (Level 6) operis (n.) work, deed, workmanship
impediō	(Page 121) (Level 6) impedīre impedīvī impedītum hinder, impede, prevent
necesse	(Page 121) (Level 6) (defective adjective) necessary, inevitable
labor	(Page 123) (Level 6) labōris (m.) difficulty, work, labor
pugna	(Page 123) (Level 6) pugnae (f.) fight

(front)	(back)
cernō	(Page 123) (Level 6) cernere crēvī crētum distinguish, discern, understand
forum	(Page 123) (Level 6) forī (n.) forum, marketplace
vīvō	(Page 125) (Level 6) vīvere vīxī vīctum live, be alive
virtūs	(Page 125) (Level 6) virtūtis (f.) manliness, courage, virtue
prīncipium	(Page 125) (Level 6) prīncipī (n.) beginning, origin
inquam	(Page 125) (Level 6) (defective verb) say

(front)	(back)
first conjugation imperfect active indicative	(Page 129) (Level 6) amābam — I was loving amābāmus — we were loving amābās — you (s.) were loving amābātis — you (pl.) were loving amābat — he (she, it) was loving amābant — they were loving
second conjugation imperfect active indicative	(Page 129) (Level 6) monēbam — I was warning monēbāmus — we were warning monēbās — you (s.) were warning monēbātis — you (pl.) were warning monēbat — he (she, it) was warning monēbant — they were warning
third conjugation imperfect active indicative	(Page 131) (Level 6) dīcēbam — I was saying dīcēbāmus — we were saying dīcēbās — you (s.) were saying dīcēbātis — you (pl.) were saying dīcēbat — he (she, it) was saying dīcēbant — they were saying
third conjugation i-stem imperfect active indicative	(Page 131) (Level 6) capiēbam — I was taking capiēbāmus — we were taking capiēbās — you (s.) were taking capiēbātis — you (pl.) were taking capiēbat — he (she, it) was taking capiēbant — they were taking
fourth conjugation imperfect active indicative	(Page 131) (Level 6) audiēbam — I was hearing audiēbāmus — we were hearing audiēbās — you (s.) were hearing audiēbātis — you (pl.) were hearing audiēbat — he (she, it) was hearing audiēbant — they were hearing
the being verb imperfect indicative	(Page 132) (Level 6) eram — I was erāmus — we were erās — you (s.) were erātis — you (pl.) were erat — he (she, it) was, there was erant — they were, there were

(front)	(back)
first conjugation imperfect passive indicative	(Page 133) (Level 6) amābar — I was being loved amābāmur — we were being loved amābāris — you (s.) were being loved amābāminī — you (pl.) were being loved amābātur — he (she, it) was being loved amābantur — they were being loved
second conjugation imperfect passive indicative	(Page 133) (Level 6) monēbar — I was being warned monēbāmur — we were being warned monēbāris — you (s.) were being warned monēbāminī — you (pl.) were being warned monēbātur — he (she, it) was being warned monēbantur — they were being warned
third conjugation imperfect passive indicative	(Page 135) (Level 6) dīcēbar — I was being told dīcēbāmur — we were being told dīcēbāris — you (s.) were being told dīcēbāminī — you (pl.) were being told dīcēbātur — he (she, it) was being told dīcēbantur — they were being told
third conjugation i-stem imperfect passive indicative	(Page 135) (Level 6) capiēbar — I was being taken capiēbāmur — we were being taken capiēbāris — you (s.) were being taken capiēbāminī — you (pl.) were being taken capiēbātur — he (she, it) was being taken capiēbantur — they were being taken
fourth conjugation imperfect passive indicative	(Page 135) (Level 6) audiēbar — I was being heard audiēbāmur — we were being heard audiēbāris — you (s.) were being heard audiēbāminī — you (pl.) were being heard audiēbātur — he (she, it) was being heard audiēbantur — they were being heard
vēndō	(Page 137) (Level 6) vēndere vēndidī vēnditum sell

(front)	(back)
vereor	(Page 137) (Level 6) verērī veritus sum fear, respect
victōria	(Page 137) (Level 6) victōriae (f.) victory
ōlim	(Page 137) (Level 6) (adverb) once, formerly, at that time, some day
cotīdiē	(Page 139) (Level 6) (adverb) daily, every day
moror	(Page 139) (Level 6) morārī morātus sum delay
signum	(Page 139) (Level 6) signī (n.) sign, signal

(front)	(back)
cōnscientia	(Page 139) (Level 6) cōnscientiae (f.) awareness, knowledge, conscience
cōgitō	(Page 141) (Level 6) cōgitāre cōgitāvī cōgitātum think, plan, consider
lavō	(Page 141) (Level 6) lavāre lāvī lautum wash
lībertās	(Page 141) (Level 6) lībertātis (f.) freedom, liberty
loquor	(Page 141) (Level 6) loquī locūtus sum speak, say, talk
māteria	(Page 143) (Level 6) māteriae (f.) material, subject matter, lumber

(front)	(back)
laus	(Page 143) (Level 6) laudis (f.) praise, fame
studium	(Page 143) (Level 6) studī (n.) eagerness, zeal, enthusiasm
cōnor	(Page 143) (Level 6) cōnārī cōnātus sum try, attempt
tēlum	(Page 145) (Level 6) tēlī (n.) offensive weapons, missiles
beneficium	(Page 145) (Level 6) beneficī (n.) kindness, favor, benefit
pōns	(Page 145) (Level 6) pontis (m.) bridge

(front)	(back)
trahō	(Page 145)　　　　　　　　　　(Level 6) trahere trāxī tractum draw, drag, lead
first conjugation future active indicative	(Page 149)　　　　　　　　　　(Level 6) amābō — I shall love　amābimus — we shall love amābis — you (s.) will love　amābitis — you (pl.) will love amābit — he (she, it) will love　amābunt — they will love
first conjugation future active infinitive	(Page 149)　　　　　　　　　　(Level 6) amātūrus [-a, -um] esse to be about to love
second conjugation future active indicative	(Page 149)　　　　　　　　　　(Level 6) monēbō — I shall warn　monēbimus — we shall warn monēbis — you (s.) will warn　monēbitis — you (pl.) will warn monēbit — he (she, it) will warn　monēbunt — they will warn
second conjugation future active infinitive	(Page 149)　　　　　　　　　　(Level 6) monitūrus [-a, -um] esse to be about to warn
third conjugation future active indicative	(Page 151)　　　　　　　　　　(Level 6) dīcam — I shall say　dīcēmus — we shall say dīcēs — you (s.) will say　dīcētis — you (pl.) will say dīcet — he (she, it) will say　dīcent — they will say

(front)	(back)

third conjugation future active infinitive	(Page 151) (Level 6) dictūrus [-a, -um] esse to be about to say
third conjugation i-stem future active indicative	(Page 151) (Level 6) capiam — I shall take capiēmus — we shall take capiēs — you (s.) will take capiētis — you (pl.) will take capiet — he (she, it) will take capient — they will take
third conjugation i-stem future active infinitive	(Page 151) (Level 6) captūrus [-a, -um] esse to be about to take
fourth conjugation future active indicative	(Page 152) (Level 6) audiam — I shall hear audiēmus — we shall hear audiēs — you (s.) will hear audiētis — you (pl.) will hear audiet — he (she, it) will hear audient — they will hear
fourth conjugation future active infinitive	(Page 152) (Level 6) auditūrus [-a, -um] esse to be about to hear
the being verb future indicative	(Page 152) (Level 6) erō — I shall be erimus — we shall be eris — you (s.) will be eritis — you (pl.) will be erit — he (she, it) will be, there will be erunt — they will be, there will be

(front)	(back)
the being verb future infinitive	(Page 152) (Level 6) futūrus [-a, -um] esse to be about to be
first conjugation future passive indicative	(Page 153) (Level 6) amābor — I shall be loved amāberis — you (s.) will be loved amābitur — he (she, it) will be loved amābimur — we shall be loved amābiminī — you (pl.) will be loved amābuntur — they will be loved
second conjugation future passive indicative	(Page 153) (Level 6) monēbor — I shall be warned monēberis — you (s.) will be warned monēbitur — he (she, it) will be warned monēbimur — we shall be warned monēbiminī — you (pl.) will be warned monēbuntur — they will be warned
third conjugation future passive indicative	(Page 155) (Level 6) dīcar — I shall be told dīcēris — you (s.) will be told dīcētur — he (she, it) will be told dīcēmur — we shall be told dīcēminī — you (pl.) will be told dīcentur — they will be told
third conjugation i-stem future passive indicative	(Page 155) (Level 6) capiar — I shall be taken capiēris — you (s.) will be taken capiētur — he (she, it) will be taken capiēmur — we shall be taken capiēminī — you (pl.) will be taken capientur — they will be taken
fourth conjugation future passive indicative	(Page 155) (Level 6) audiar — I shall be heard audiēris — you (s.) will be heard audiētur — he (she, it) will be heard audiēmur — we shall be heard audiēminī — you (pl.) will be heard audientur — they will be heard